WeightWatchers® momentum™

HEALTHY COOKING BASICS

10 **Must-Know Techniques** **175** **Recipes for Creating Delicious Meals**

From
Kim

About Weight Watchers

Weight Watchers International, Inc., is the world's leading provider of weight-management services, operating globally through a network of company-owned and franchise operations. Weight Watchers holds over 50,000 weekly meetings worldwide, at which members receive group support and education about healthful eating patterns, behavior modification, and physical activity. Weight-loss and weight-management results vary by individual. We recommend that you attend Weight Watchers meetings to benefit from the supportive environment you'll find there and follow the comprehensive Weight Watchers program, which includes a food plan, an activity plan, and a behavioral component. In addition, Weight Watchers offers a wide range of products, publications, and programs for people interested in weight loss and weight control. For the Weight Watchers meeting nearest you, call **1-800-651-6000.** For information about bringing Weight Watchers to your workplace, call **1-800-8AT-WORK.** Also visit us at our Web site, **WeightWatchers.com,** and look for **Weight Watchers Magazine** at your newsstand or in your meeting room.

ASIAN BEEF AND BOK
CHOY SALAD, PAGE 111

WEIGHT WATCHERS PUBLISHING GROUP

EDITORIAL DIRECTOR	NANCY GAGLIARDI
CREATIVE DIRECTOR	ED MELNITSKY
PHOTO EDITOR	DEBORAH HARDT
MANAGING EDITOR	SARAH WHARTON
PRODUCTION MANAGER	ALAN BIEDERMAN
EDITORIAL ASSISTANT	KRISTINA LUCARELLI
FOOD EDITOR	EILEEN RUNYAN
EDITOR	JACKIE MILLS
NUTRITION CONSULTANT	U. BEATE KRINKE
PHOTOGRAPHER	IAIN BAGWELL
FOOD STYLIST	SALLY JO O'BRIEN
PROP STYLIST	PAIGE HICKS
FRONT COVER DESIGN	SHELLEY CAMHI
ART DIRECTOR	DANIELA HRITCU
ILLUSTRATOR	BOB ECKSTEIN
ADDITIONAL PHOTOGRAPHY	DASHA WRIGHT
	HAYLEY HARRISON
	RITA MAAS

About Our Recipes

We make every effort to ensure that you will have success with our recipes. For best results and for nutritional accuracy, please keep these guidelines in mind:

● Recipes in this book have been developed for members who are following the **Momentum**™ plan. We include **POINTS**® values for every recipe. **POINTS** values are assigned based on calories, fat (grams), and fiber (grams) provided for a serving size of a recipe.

● All recipes feature approximate nutritional information; our recipes are analyzed for Calories (Cal), Total Fat (Fat), Saturated Fat (Sat Fat), Trans Fat (Trans Fat), Cholesterol (Chol), Sodium (Sod), Carbohydrates (Carb), Dietary Fiber (Fib), Protein (Prot), and Calcium (Calc).

● Nutritional information for recipes that include meat, poultry, and fish are based on cooked skinless boneless portions (unless otherwise stated), with the fat trimmed.

● We recommend that you buy lean meat and poultry, then trim it of all visible fat before cooking. When poultry is cooked with the skin on, we suggest removing the skin before eating.

● Before serving, divide foods—including any vegetables, accompaniments, or sauce—into portions of equal size according to the designated number of servings per recipe.

● Any substitutions made to the ingredients will alter the "Per serving" nutritional information and may affect the **POINTS** value.

● All fresh fruits, vegetables, and greens in recipes should be rinsed before using.

● All ◆™ **Filling Extra** suggestions have a **POINTS** value of **0** unless otherwise stated.

● All **Filling Foods** are highlighted in green.

● Recipes that work with the **Simply Filling technique** are indicated.

SPINACH, ARTICHOKE, AND
OLIVE PIZZA, PAGE 102

Contents

**PEANUT BUTTER AND CHOCOLATE
CUPCAKES, PAGE 229**

Kitchen Basics

If you're just learning to cook, here's the place to start. Find out which tools and appliances are must-haves for a well-equipped kitchen. Learn how to stock your pantry with the healthiest foods. Then put all that knowledge to use with ten easy cooking techniques that will help you make delicious and satisfying meals your whole family will love.

Kitchen Tools

With the right tools, any job is easier. When stocking your kitchen, buy the best-quality tools you can afford because you'll be using them almost every day.

MUST HAVE

A **box grater** has four sides with a sturdy handle on top to finely or coarsely grate or shred vegetables, cheeses, and citrus zest.

A must-have tool for opening canned foods, the best designed **can openers** have a cushioned knob and handles for easy operation. Buy one with a rust-proof stainless steel cutting blade.

Ideal for small amounts of juice, a **citrus reamer** is a small cone-shaped tool with a pointed end and deep furrows. As a stand-in for a reamer, insert a fork into a lemon half and squeeze to extract the juice.

A **colander** lets you separate liquids from solids. You will use it nearly every day for draining cooked pasta and vegetables, draining washed greens, or rinsing fresh berries.

Cooling racks allow air circulation while baked goods cool. Round wire racks are good for cooling round cake layers. Large rectangular cooling racks are perfect for cooling large quantities of cookies or large cakes.

Choose a **cutting board** made of wood or plastic. Avoid ceramic, as it does not absorb the impact of the knife blade, making it more difficult to chop food and may damage knives.

Three knives are essential: a **small paring knife**, which is 3 to 4 inches long and used for peeling and slicing small foods, an 8- or 9-inch **cook's knife**, used for all basic chopping, dicing, and slicing, and a **serrated knife** for slicing bread.

For serving soup, chili, or oatmeal or for adding broth to risotto without dripping or spilling, a **ladle** is essential.

To measure dry ingredients accurately, use a standard **set of nesting measuring cups** of $1/4$-, $1/3$-, $1/2$- and 1-cup sizes. To measure wet ingredients, use **glass or plastic measuring cups.** It is essential to have a 1-cup glass measure and nice to also have 2- and 4-cup measures.

Measuring spoons come in nesting sets of $1/8$ teaspoon, $1/4$ teaspoon, $1/2$ teaspoon, 1 teaspoon, and 1 tablespoon.

A nesting set of glass or stainless-steel **mixing bowls** are the workhorses of any kitchen. Plastic bowls are not recommended as they absorb flavors and fats.

Use a **pastry brush** for applying an egg white glaze onto breads or pastries, brushing syrup over warm cake or muffins, or for basting meats and poultry.

There are several styles of **potato mashers**, but all make quick work of mashing cooked potatoes and other root vegetables.

Rolling pins come with and without handles. Both styles work well. Keep in mind that the heavier the pin, the less effort it takes to roll out dough.

Kitchen shears are ideal for cutting paper to line cake pans, cutting up a chicken, clipping kitchen string, mincing chives, and hundreds of other everyday uses. Choose shears made of stainless steel so that they don't rust.

Use a **coarse-mesh sieve** for sifting flour, cocoa, and confectioners' sugar and a fine-mesh sieve for straining stocks and separating fruit purees from their seeds. It's a good idea to have a few sizes.

An **instant-read thermometer** gives a temperature reading in a matter of seconds. The thermometer is inserted into the center of meat or poultry (without touching a bone) to ensure that the food is cooked to the proper temperature (see page 113 for a chart of minimum safe cooking temperatures).

A **swivel-bladed vegetable peeler** makes quick work of peeling fruits and vegetables without removing too much peel or skin.

Spatulas come in different shapes for different tasks. A flat, wide metal spatula is good for turning fish, and other flat foods. A rubber spatula is used for mixing batters. A silicone (heatproof) spatula has the flexibility of a rubber spatula and can withstand temperatures up to 800°F.

To make sure your foods are cooked to the correct doneness, a **kitchen timer** is essential. Always set the timer for the least amount of time recommended in the recipe to avoid overcooking.

A **slotted spoon** makes it easy to lift a piece of pasta or a vegetable from boiling water to test for doneness.

Spring-loaded tongs are the best tool for lifting and moving food and can be locked shut for easy storage. Use silicone-tipped tongs in nonstick cookware to prevent scratching.

A **medium-size whisk** is a must-have for whipping up egg whites, mixing salad dressings, producing smooth gravies and sauces, and making pancake and quick bread batters.

Have a few **wooden spoons** in your kitchen for stirring anything and everything. They don't transfer heat, so your hand stays cool while stirring and they won't scratch your pots.

A plastic **salad spinner** uses centrifugal force to remove most of the water from washed greens, herbs, or fresh berries. They are available in several sizes.

Fat Separator
Perfect for making pan gravy, a fat separator has a sharply angled spout set at the base. The fat floats to the top of the separator and you can pour off the fat-free pan juices, leaving the fat behind.

Pastry Blender
The curved wires of this classic baking tool easily cut butter and vegetable shortening into dry ingredients for biscuits, scones, and pie crusts, ensuring a flaky result.

Garlic Press
This hinged tool squeezes garlic into smaller pieces than can be achieved from mincing. Because more surface area of the garlic is exposed when it is pushed through a press, the flavor is more pronounced.

Rasp Grater
Originally made for woodworkers to smooth the rough edges of wood, this handy grater can be used for grating citrus zest, whole nutmeg, chocolate, and hard cheeses.

Mandoline
Also called a vegetable slicer, this sharp-bladed counter-top tool slices, cuts French fries, and juliennes firm fruits and vegetables, including apple, onion, potato, and zucchini from ultra thin to thick in record time.

Appliances

Beyond the must-haves, your appliances should reflect the way you cook. If you do a lot of baking, a stand mixer is essential. If you're the kind of cook who likes to throw everything in one pot, then a slow cooker is perfect for you.

MUST HAVE	NICE TO HAVE

Blender

This kitchen workhorse blends and purees foods in an instant. Look for a model that comes apart easily for quick clean up. If you make big batches of soups or smoothies, buy a large capacity blender.

Good Idea: Use a blender to make silky soups and sauces, flavorful pestos and salad dressings and refreshing fruit smoothies.

Bread Machine

Enjoy home-baked bread without effort with a countertop bread machine. Put in the ingredients, turn on the machine, and walk away. Some models offer a variety of loaf sizes and up to 16 pre-set options for a variety of breads and rolls.

Good Idea: The machine can be used to mix up small or large batches of your favorite cookie dough using the dough cycle, then shape the dough and bake in a regular oven.

Handheld Electric Mixer

Handheld mixers are small, lightweight, and easy to store. The latest models are packed with power and have several speed settings.

Good Idea: Use a mixer for making fluffy and light mashed potatoes, beating egg whites, mixing soft doughs and batters, and making frostings.

Coffee/Spice Grinder

This handy little appliance grinds whole spices—and coffee beans—with the touch of a button.

Good Idea: To clean the grinder between grinding spices and coffee beans, grind up some uncooked rice. Discard the rice and brush away any residue with a pastry brush.

Microwave

You will use this can't-live-without-it appliance several times every day. The newest models have pre-programmed times for making popcorn, defrosting, and cooking various leftover and frozen foods.

Good Idea: A microwave is indispensible for tasks like melting butter and chocolate and heating leftovers. But it's also great for cooking fish fillets to perfection and making simple vegetable side dishes in minutes.

Electric Griddle

An electric griddle is convenient to have if you frequently cook grilled breakfast foods or grill sandwiches for your family. Some come with backsplashes, which prevent foods from sliding off when turned, as well as a nonstick surface, which ensures easy clean up.

Good Idea: Use the griddle to cook large batches of pancakes, eggs, bacon, french toast, or grilled sandwiches. Since you can cook a lot of food at once, you won't have to worry about keeping food warm between batches.

Food Processor

This efficient machine performs a variety of tasks, including grating, slicing, chopping, and pureeing. Most models come with a plastic mixing blade, a steel chopping blade, and one or two shredding and slicing blades. They are dishwasher safe.

Good Idea: Use the food processor to quickly cut butter or shortening into flour when you make biscuits or pie crust.

Rice Cooker

A rice cooker takes the guesswork out of cooking rice perfectly every time. With one of these appliances, you can put an end to gummy rice and messy boilovers.

Good Idea: Rice cookers cook brown rice perfectly. Cook a large batch on the weekend to use throughout the week for an effortless healthy side dish.

Immersion Blender

Also known as a wand or handheld blender, this small appliance has an extended blade that can be immersed in any size pot or bowl for easy blending or pureeing.

Good Idea: Buy an immersion blender with a chopper attachment. It will allow you to chop fresh herbs and garlic in seconds.

Slow Cooker

Slow cookers are a lifesaver for working moms. With a few minutes prep in the morning, you can come home to a comforting meal that's ready to serve.

Good Idea: Use a slow cooker to make long-cooking soups, stews, and braise meats and poultry. Try it for making steel-cut oatmeal, dried beans, and beef or chicken stock too.

Panini Press

This popular appliances turns out grilled sandwiches that are crispy on the outside and moist on the inside without crushing the bread. Most have nonstick surfaces for easy clean up.

Good Idea: A panini press makes it easy to cook up a large or small batch of crispy bacon, while the fat drips into the detachable fat catcher.

Stand Mixer

A heavy-duty stand mixer is a must if you do a lot of baking. They usually come with 3 attachments: a paddle for making batters, a whisk attachment for beating egg whites, and a dough hook for making yeast dough.

Good Idea: If you love homemade bread—but don't like to knead or the boxy shape of loaves baked in a bread machine—a stand mixer with a dough hook attachment is a blessing. Dump the dough ingredients in the mixer and knead at low speed with the dough hook, let the dough rise, and then form it into any shape you like.

Healthy Pantry

Use these charts as a guide to storing staples safely. If a food doesn't have a sell-by date, affix a label to the package and mark the date you bought it so you'll know when it's past its prime.

SHELF STAPLES

Food	Storage Time	Storage Tips
Canned tuna and salmon	Unopened, 1 year; opened, 2 days refrigerated	After opening, immediately transfer to airtight container and refrigerate.
Canned dried beans	Unopened, 1 year; opened, 3 days refrigerated	After opening, refrigerate in airtight container; do not keep in original can.
Brown rice (including basmati and jasmine)	6 months	Brown rice still has its nutritious bran layer intact. Because of the oil in the bran, brown rice will not keep as long as white rice.
Whole wheat pastas	1 year	Store in the original container in a cool, dry place.
Barley	6 months	For longer storage, store in an airtight container in the refrigerator.
Oats	6 months	Store oats in the original container in a cool, dark place.
Whole wheat couscous	6 months	If you live in a humid climate, transfer the couscous to an airtight container for storage.
Dried beans and lentils	1 year	Store in the plastic bag they are packaged in. Never store in the refrigerator; beans can absorb moisture and spoil.
Honey, maple syrup, molasses	2 years	If sugar crystals form, place the container in warm water and stir until the crystals dissolve.

BAKING STAPLES

Food	Storage Time	Storage Tips
All-purpose flour	1 year at room temperature; up to 2 years frozen	Store flour in a cool dry place.
Whole wheat flour	1-3 months at room temperature; 6 months refrigerated; 1 year frozen	Transfer flour to an airtight container to preserve moisture content.
White and confectioners' sugar	2 years	To protect against humidity, store sugar in an airtight container.
Light and dark brown sugar	4-6 months	Brown sugar dries out quickly; store the sugar in an airtight container after opening package.
Baking powder, baking soda	12-18 months	Store tightly covered in a cool dry place.
Unsweetened cocoa powder	1 year	Store at room temperature in the original container.
Chocolate chips, baking chocolate	1 year	Store all chocolate in a cool dry place. A white film sometimes appears on the surface caused by temperature fluctuations; it does not affect the taste or quality.
Nuts	Unopened, 1 year; opened 3 months	Store in airtight container.

REFRIGERATOR STAPLES

Food	Storage Time	Storage Tips
Pickles, olives, capers	Unopened, 1 year; opened, 1-2 months refrigerated	Keep jar tightly capped; discard if salt crystals accumulate at top of jar.
Salsa	Unopened, 1 year; opened, 1 month refrigerated	If mold forms around the edge of the salsa, discard the entire jar.
Mustard, ketchup	Unopened, 1 year; opened, 3 months refrigerated	Since these foods contain acid, they are less prone to spoilage and can be stored in the door (the warmest part) of the refrigerator.
Reduced-fat and fat-free mayonnaise	Unopened, 1 year; opened, 2 months refrigerated	For best quality and freshness, always check the "use by" date on mayonnaise.
Reduced-sodium soy sauce	Unopened, 1 year; opened, 6 months refrigerated	Always store opened soy sauce in the fridge to preserve the flavor.
Worcestershire sauce, hot pepper sauce	Unopened, 1 year; opened, 6 months refrigerated	Wipe off the bottles after each use to prevent drips in the refrigerator.
Jellies and jams	Unopened, 1 year; opened, 6 months refrigerated	Wipe off the rim of the jar before replacing the lid after each use to prevent sticky build up.
Whole wheat tortillas	2 months	After opening, store tightly sealed in the original package.

FREEZER STAPLES

Food	Storage Time	Storage Tips
Steaks and roasts	2-3 days refrigerated; 6-8 months frozen	Freeze in zip-close plastic freezer bags to maintain maximum freshness
Ground beef	1-2 days refrigerated; 3-4 months frozen	Always label and date frozen foods so you will eat them before they start losing quality.
Pork chops	2-3 days refrigerated; 4-6 months frozen	Buy chops in a single layer tray; freeze on tray. Remove packaging and put frozen chops in a zip-close plastic freezer bag; return to freezer. They will remain in individual servings.
Skinless boneless chicken breasts	1-2 days refrigerated; 9 months frozen	Individually wrap chicken breasts for easy thawing.
Skinless fish fillets	1 day refrigerated; 3 months frozen	Place fish in a sealed container in refrigerator to stop the juices from dripping on other foods.
Peeled shrimp	1-2 days refrigerated; 3 months frozen	Don't freeze fresh shrimp. Most likely they have already been frozen and thawed for retail sale.
Frozen fruits and vegetables	9 months	Store in the original bag or box.

10 Healthy Cooking Techniques

Sauté

To cook food quickly in a skillet over medium-high heat in a small amount of oil.

- The French verb *sauter* means to jump, which is what the food seems to do in the skillet when it is sautéed.
- Sautéing browns meats and fish on the outside while cooking them through. Sliced or cut-up vegetables can be sautéed until just crisp-tender.
- The food is turned often, or stirred, depending on the size of the pieces.

HOW TO... Sauté

1

Heat small amount of oil in nonstick skillet over medium-high heat until oil is hot (2 teaspoons oil is enough for 12-inch skillet). Season meats or seafood or dredge in seasoned flour and add to skillet. For vegetables, just add them to skillet. Wait 1–2 minutes to turn or stir. Meats and seafood should develop a brown crust before turning.

2

Turn meats several times (fish is the exception; since it is delicate, turn it only once) and stir vegetables often until desired degree of doneness is reached. Remove food from pan. Sautéed meats and seafood leave behind flavorful browned bits, which make for the start of a tasty sauce. You can add about 1/2 cup broth, wine, or fruit juice to pan, bring it to boil, and simmer, scraping bottom to release browned bits. Simmer until liquid is reduced by about half.

What You Need

A large heavy-bottomed nonstick skillet or sauté pan big enough to hold the food you are cooking in a single layer with at least 1 inch between the pieces. The nonstick surface allows you to use less oil than you would with a regular skillet. You'll also need either plastic-tipped tongs for turning or a wooden spoon or silicone spatula for turning or stirring the food without harming the surface of the nonstick skillet.

What to Try

- Thin, tender cuts of beef, such as filets mignons
- Boneless center-cut pork chops
- Skinless, boneless chicken breasts (whole or cut into small pieces)
- Fish fillets and shrimp
- Tender, quick-cooking vegetables

Make It Flavorful

- After sautéing pork chops or chicken breasts, quickly sauté thinly sliced onions or bell peppers in the same skillet for a fast and flavorful topping.
- Coat tilapia or catfish fillets with cornmeal seasoned with cumin, chili powder, and salt before sautéing.
- Stir chopped fresh flat-leaf parsley or basil into sautéed cherry tomatoes, asparagus, zucchini, or yellow squash just before serving.

Stir-Fry

To cook small pieces of food quickly in a small amount of oil in a wok or large skillet over medium-high heat.

- The food is stirred constantly, so that meats and shellfish brown on the outside while cooking on the inside, remaining moist and tender.
- For a stir-fry, choose foods that cook in about the same amount of time.
- This Asian cooking technique uses small amounts of fat and the fast cooking retains maximum nutrients, making it very healthy.

HOW TO... Stir-Fry

1

All ingredients should be prepared before cooking begins and placed near the stove. Foods should be thinly sliced or cut into small even-size pieces so they cook quickly and uniformly. Heat nonstick wok or large, deep nonstick skillet over medium-high heat. When a drop of water sizzles when dropped on surface, add just enough canola oil to lightly coat wok (2 teaspoons oil will coat 12-inch wok).

2

Add the food to the wok and stir-fry, moving the pieces constantly, just until done, 3–5 minutes. Beef and pork can be cooked until just slightly pink in the middle, chicken should be cooked through with no pink juices, and shellfish should be opaque.

What You Need

A large nonstick wok or a large, deep nonstick skillet that is roomy enough to hold the food without crowding. The nonstick surface allows you to use less oil than you would in a regular wok or skillet. If you use a skillet, choose one at least 2½ inches deep to have enough room to stir the food as it cooks. You'll also need a wooden spoon or silicone spatula for stirring the food without harming the surface of the wok or skillet.

What to Try

- Tender cuts of lean meats, such as flank steak, sirloin, center-cut pork chops, and pork tenderloin, cut into chunks or strips
- Chunks or strips of skinless boneless chicken breasts, skinless boneless chicken thighs, and turkey cutlets
- Shrimp and scallops
- Firm or extra-firm tofu, cut into cubes
- Tender, quick-cooking vegetables

Make It Flavorful

- Toss thinly sliced sirloin, skinless, boneless chicken breasts, or shrimp in 1 teaspoon of Asian (dark) sesame oil before cooking.
- Sprinkle chicken, pork, or shrimp with five-spice powder before stir-frying.
- Add chopped fresh cilantro or thinly sliced basil to a stir-fry dish just before serving.

Pan Sear

To cook food in a skillet over medium-high heat using very little oil for a short amount of time.

- The food is only turned once, searing it on the outside to create a flavorful crust and keeping the inside of the food moist.
- Searing releases juices to the surface of the food, where they caramelize, giving good color and flavor to the dish.
- Since so little added fat is necessary, this is a perfect technique for healthy cooking—especially when you need to make dinner in a hurry.

HOW TO... Pan Sear

1

Heat a large heavy-bottomed skillet over medium-high heat until a drop of water sizzles when dropped onto the surface, about 5 minutes. Add just enough canola oil to lightly coat the bottom (1 teaspoon of oil will coat a 12-inch skillet). Season the food and add it to the skillet. Wait 2–3 minutes for the color of the food to begin to change from the bottom up: Seafood will turn opaque; beef and pork will turn brown. Then turn the food over.

2

Continue cooking to the desired doneness, which depends on the food. A 4-ounce pork chop will take another 3–4 minutes, a 4-ounce fillet mignon will take another 2–3 minutes, scallops will take another 1–2 minutes. Remove the food from the pan to serving plates as soon as it is done to prevent overcooking. For larger steaks that will be sliced before serving, let stand on a cutting board 5 minutes before slicing.

What You Need

A heavy-bottomed skillet big enough to hold the food you are cooking in a single layer with at least 1 inch between the pieces. A cast iron or stainless steel skillet is an excellent choice.

What to Try

- Thin, tender, quick-cooking steaks such as filet mignon, sirloin, top round, and flank steak
- Thin pork, lamb, and veal chops
- Fish fillets and scallops

Make It Flavorful

- Sprinkle steaks, chops, or seafood with a spice blend before pan searing try Cajun seasoning blend on salmon fillets, fajita seasoning on steaks, or Caribbean jerk seasoning on pork chops.
- Sprinkle any meats, poultry, fish, or shrimp with salt and cracked black pepper before pan searing for a simple yet flavor-enhancing seasoning.
- Serve pan seared foods with a purchased or homemade salsa.

Steam

To cook food in a basket above simmering water in a covered saucepan.

• Steaming cooks foods gently without them coming into contact with water, so the fresh flavor of the food is retained.

• Steaming preserves the nutrients and bright color of foods while cooking with no added fat.

• Take care when steaming, as the steam is very hot. Open the lid away from you so the steam is not released toward you.

HOW TO... Steam

1

Pour about 1 inch of water into a large pot and bring to a boil. There should be enough water to cook the food without boiling away quickly, but not so much that the water touches the food in the basket. More water may be added during the process in the case of foods that take longer to cook. Place the food in the basket, carefully set it over the water, and cover the saucepan with the lid. Adjust the heat so that the water is bubbling but not at a rolling boil.

2

Cook the food to the desired degree of doneness. Vegetables such as green beans, squash, and snow peas should be crisp and brightly colored. Potatoes, winter squash, and beets should be fork-tender. Fish and shellfish should be opaque, and chicken should be cooked through with no pink juices. Remove the food from the steamer basket as soon as it is done to prevent overcooking.

What You Need

A collapsible steamer basket and a saucepan with a tight-fitting lid or a large pot with a steamer basket insert. You can also steam food in a tiered bamboo steamer set inside a wok or skillet of boiling water.

What to Try

• Skinless boneless chicken breasts
• Fish fillets, shrimp, and scallops
• Almost all vegetables

Make It Flavorful

• Add sliced onions, crushed garlic cloves, or slices of fresh ginger to the steaming water to infuse food with great taste.
• Sprinkle wedges of butternut or acorn squash with ground cinnamon before steaming.
• Line the steamer basket with fresh herb sprigs; then top with the food to add a punch of herbal flavor.

Boil and Simmer

To cook foods such as pasta or vegetables until tender in a pot of boiling water.

- Large bubbles should constantly break the surface of the water when food is boiled.
- Simmering cooks foods in water that is just below the boiling point. Tiny bubbles should frequently break the surface of the water.
- Many foods, such as long-cooking grains and dried beans, are first brought to a boil, then simmered to finish cooking.

HOW TO... Boil and Simmer

1

For pastas and quick-cooking vegetables, fill a large pot two thirds full with water and bring to a boil. Add the food and cook, uncovered, until tender. For foods that take longer to cook, such as potatoes, beets, grains, and dried beans, add them to the pot with cold water and bring to a boil (grains and beans are cooked in a specific amount of water). Reduce heat, cover, and simmer until tender.

2

To test the food for doneness, remove a piece with a slotted spoon. Pastas should be tender, yet firm to the bite. Vegetables such as broccoli and green beans should be crisp-tender. Dense vegetables should be cooked until fork-tender. Cook grains and dried beans until they are tender, yet hold their shape.

What You Need

All that's required for boiling or simmering is a pot with a lid that is large enough to hold the food without overcrowding. Pasta and vegetables cook more evenly when they are in a pot large enough to move freely and grains and dried beans need lots of room to expand, so select a pot accordingly.

What to Try

- Pastas
- Almost all vegetables
- Grains
- Dried beans

Make It Flavorful

- Salting the cooking water for pasta and vegetables is a matter of taste, but the general recommendation is 1 tablespoon of salt for 4 quarts of water.
- Cook dried beans, rice, and grains in chicken or vegetable broth to enhance the flavor.
- Add a cinnamon stick and a slice of fresh ginger to the pot when cooking rice for a flavorful accompaniment to Indian dishes.
- A drizzle of extra-virgin olive oil and a sprinkle of salt and freshly ground pepper are all you need to turn plain boiled vegetables or pasta into a simple, yet tasty side dish.

Braise

To cook meats or poultry by browning on the stovetop then slowly baking in simmering liquid.

• Browning foods first imparts them with rich flavor which then transfers to the braising liquid.

• Braising is an economical way of cooking, since the best meats to braise are often the most inexpensive.

• Braising uses very little added fat and transforms lean, often tough cuts of meat into tender and flavorful meals.

HOW TO... Braise

1

Heat a small amount of oil in a Dutch oven over medium-high heat until the oil is hot. Season the meat and add it to the pot (2 teaspoons of oil is enough for a large pot). Wait 1–2 minutes for a brown crust to develop; then turn to brown it on all sides. Add enough cooking liquid to reach about halfway up the meat and scrape the pot to release the browned bits from the bottom. Sturdy, aromatic vegetables such as onions, carrots, and celery make good additions to braised meats.

2

Bake, covered, at 350°F until very tender, 2–3 hours. Depending on the type of dish, you may thicken the broth with a mixture of flour and water or cornstarch and water, or you can simply serve the meat and vegetables with the cooking liquid.

What You Need

For braising, you'll need a Dutch oven or a large pot that has a tight-fitting lid and can go from stovetop to oven. Choose a pot large enough to hold one-pot meals of meat or poultry and lots of vegetables.

What to Try

• Large cuts of meats that take a long time to cook, such as top or bottom round beef roast, beef brisket, well-trimmed Boston butt pork roast, or well-trimmed lamb shoulder or lamb shanks

• Skinless boneless chicken thighs and skinless chicken legs

Make It Flavorful

• Use a flavorful broth or stock, wine, beer, or fruit or vegetable juice to deepen the flavor of the braising liquid.

• Add dried herbs at the beginning of cooking to allow them to soften and release their flavors (try dried Italian seasoning, oregano, or basil), or add fresh herbs at the end of cooking to take advantage of their bright flavors (try flat-leaf parsley, rosemary, or chives).

• Season the meat with spices before the browning step. Try a combination of chili powder and cumin to add Tex-Mex flavors, coriander and ginger for a Moroccan meal, or sprinkling of curry powder for an Indian–inspired dish.

Roast

To cook foods in an uncovered roasting pan in the oven.

- Roasted meats and poultry have a well-browned crust and are moist and juicy on the inside.
- Roasting is a carefree method of cooking, since you usually turn or stir the food only once or twice during cooking.
- Roasting concentrates the natural sugars in vegetables, caramelizing the outside and intensifying their flavors.

HOW TO... Roast

1

To reduce fat and calories, trim any visible fat on meats before roasting. Leave the skin on poultry to preserve moisture while roasting, but remove it before eating. Cut vegetables into uniform-size pieces for even cooking. Season all foods before roasting and toss vegetables with a small amount of oil to help with browning. Meats do not need oil added to them before roasting.

2

Meats and poultry generally roast at temperatures between 350°F and 375°F (larger meats roast at lower temperatures) and vegetables at 400°F to 425°F. Poultry should be cooked until an instant-read thermometer reaches 165°F when inserted into the center of the thigh. Beef should reach 160°F for medium and 145°F for medium-rare, when a thermometer is inserted in the center. Pork should reach 160°F.

What You Need

For roasting meats and poultry, you'll need a low-sided roasting pan with a rack that fits inside the pan. Placing meat and poultry on a rack allows the heat to circulate around it for even cooking and browning. An instant-read thermometer is essential to establish the proper degree of doneness for meats and poultry. For roasting vegetables, you'll need a shallow, rimmed baking pan large enough to hold the vegetables in a single layer.

What to Try

- Large tender cuts of meats such as beef tenderloin, eye of round beef roast, pork loin, pork tenderloin, and rack of lamb
- Whole chickens
- Almost all vegetables

Make It Flavorful

- Use your favorite dry rub or low-fat marinade to add extra flavor to meats. Always discard the marinade and blot the meat dry with paper towels before roasting.
- Infuse meats with garlicky flavor by cutting small slits in the meat. Insert a thin slice of garlic into each slit and roast.
- To boost the flavor of roasted root vegetables, drizzle them with a teaspoon of honey, molasses, or maple syrup after roasting and toss to coat.

Broil

To cook food on a rack beneath a heat source.

- Broiling on a rack allows fats from meat or poultry to drip to the bottom of the pan, saving calories. Line the broiler pan with foil for easy clean up.

- When broiled, tender quick-cooking vegetables, such as sliced bell peppers, onions, or zucchini, are delicious with lightly charred edges and tender centers.

- Broiling is a quick and simple way of cooking a variety of foods that uses little or no added fat.

HOW TO... Broil

1

Adjust the oven rack so that the food in the pan under the broiler is about 5 inches away from the heat source. If the food is too close, it will burn on the outside before it gets done on the inside. Preheat the broiler for at least 5 minutes before cooking. Spray the broiler rack with nonstick spray. Season the food and place it on the rack.

2

Broil the food to the desired degree of doneness, taking into consideration that thicker pieces of meats and poultry will take longer to cook. Delicate fish fillets do not need to be turned while broiling, but all other foods should be turned once for even cooking. Because broiling is done at such high temperatures, watch the food carefully as it is cooking to prevent burning.

What You Need

A broiler pan: A large, shallow drip pan topped with a slotted rack to allow fats to drain away as the food cooks. If you don't have a broiler pan, you can improvise with a flat roasting rack or a heavy-gauge cooling rack set inside a baking pan. You can also broil food, particularly fish, in a shallow baking pan without the rack.

What to Try

- Thin, tender steaks, such as flank steak, sirloin, top round, and filets mignons
- Pork chops and lamb chops
- Fish fillets, shrimp, and scallops
- Kebabs made with tender chunks of beef, pork, chicken breast, or shrimp alternated on skewers with chunks of vegetables
- Tender, quick-cooking vegetables

Make It Flavorful

- Make a simple rub for 4 steaks by combining 1 teaspoon kosher salt, $\frac{1}{2}$ teaspoon cracked black peppercorns, and $\frac{1}{8}$ teaspoon cayenne. Rub the mixture over both sides of the meat before broiling.
- Stir together 2 tablespoons Dijon mustard and 1 tablespoon honey and brush over pork chops, shrimp, or salmon fillets before broiling.
- Spread fish fillets with a thin layer of purchased basil pesto before broiling.

Grill

To cook food on a grill rack over a charcoal or gas fire.

- Grilling sears food, leaving the outside browned and caramelized and the interior juicy and tender.
- The smoky, lightly charred flavors that grilling imparts is delicious in almost any kind of meat, seafood, or vegetable.
- It requires very little added fat and adds delicious smoky flavor, making it ideal for preparing healthy meals.

HOW TO... Grill

1

Marinate or season foods before grilling (see page 140). Spray the grill rack with nonstick spray before lighting the fire. Prepare a charcoal fire or preheat a gas grill. A charcoal fire is ready for cooking when the coals have a light coating of white ash. Gas grills take about 15 minutes to preheat.

2

Place meats and vegetables on the grill rack, and grill. Toss vegetables with a light coating of oil (1 teaspoon of oil will coat about 4 cups of vegetables). Sturdy fish, such as salmon or tuna, and large pieces of vegetables can be placed directly on the grill rack. Place delicate fish fillets and small pieces of vegetables in a grill basket to keep them intact and to prevent them from falling through the grill rack. Turn the food at least once for even cooking and cook to the desired degree of doneness. If the food is browning too quickly, move it to the edge of the grill where the temperature is lower.

What You Need

A charcoal or gas grill and a long-handled metal turner or tongs for turning the food. You'll also need an instant-read thermometer to establish the proper degree of doneness for meats and poultry.

What to Try

- Thin, tender cuts of meat, such as steaks and chops
- Burgers
- Skinless boneless chicken breasts and skinless boneless chicken thighs
- Fish fillets, and steaks, shrimp, and scallops
- Tender, quick-cooking vegetables

Make It Flavorful

- Marinate meats and poultry in your favorite mixture of citrus juices and herbs for at least an hour or up to overnight to soak up flavor.
- If you're in a hurry, or have forgotten to marinate, rub meat or poultry with a blend of dried spices and seasonings to add flavor instantly.
- To infuse wood smoke flavor into foods, soak 1 cup of hickory or mesquite chips in water for about 1 hour. Drain them and toss on top of the charcoal just before grilling. If you're using a gas grill, put the soaked wood chips in a disposable pan with holes poked in it and place the pan on the lit burner.

Bake

To cook food in the dry heat of the oven.

- Baking is usually done at a lower temperature than roasting, but results in foods with similarly caramelized flavors.
- Many desserts and breads as well as some meat, poultry, and seafood dishes can be baked.
- Baking gives all foods a browned exterior and a tender interior.

HOW TO... Bake

1

Unless otherwise specified in the recipe, place the oven rack in the center of the oven. Preheat the oven. Spray the pan or baking dish with nonstick spray. Spoon cake batters into the pans evenly; spread thick batters evenly. For muffins, fill the tins two thirds full. Season meats, poultry, and seafood and place in a single layer in a baking dish. Bake casseroles in a baking dish that holds the food with room to spare so that liquids do not bubble over in the oven.

2

To determine the doneness of cakes, or muffins, insert a toothpick into the center; it should come out clean with no crumbs clinging. Beef and pork can be baked until slightly pink in the middle, chicken should be cooked through with no pink juices, and fish should be opaque in the center. Vegetables, such as potatoes or winter squash should be tender when pierced with a knife.

What You Need

For making baked goods and desserts, you will need a variety of baking pans. Shiny metal pans are best for cakes and muffins because they reflect heat and create a light brown crust. Dark metal pans absorb heat, so foods brown faster and develop a darker crust. For baking meats, poultry, seafood, and casseroles, use ovenproof glass, enamel-coated cast iron, and porcelain baking dishes.

What to Try

- Breads
- Cakes, muffins, pies, and other desserts
- Meat, poultry, seafood, and vegetable dishes
- Casseroles, stuffings, and pizzas

Make It Flavorful

- When baking chicken breasts or thighs, rub the seasonings under the skin and bake with the skin on to preserve moisture. Remove the skin before eating.
- Give baked fish fillets flavor and crunch by coating them before baking with an egg beaten with a little water, then with cornmeal, crushed cornflake cereal, seasoned bread crumbs, or panko bread crumbs.
- To add crunchy sweetness to a dozen muffins, sprinkle the top of the batter evenly with 2 teaspoons sugar just before baking.

CHAPTER 1

Stocks, Dressings & Sauces

Forget canned broths, bottled dressings, and squeeze-bottle sauces. With these no-fuss recipes, you can stock your refrigerator and freezer with homemade versions of indispensable staples that taste much better than the store-bought variety. Make healthful weeknight dinners in a hurry with these culinary building blocks.

Vegetable Stock

(0 POINTS VALUE)

level	technique	prep	cook	serves
Basic	Simmer pg. 22	15 min	45 min	6

- ◆ 1 large onion, chopped
- ◆ 1 large leek, cleaned and chopped (white and green parts)
- ◆ 2 celery stalks, with leaves, chopped
- ◆ 2 carrots, sliced
- ◆ 1 russet potato, scrubbed and chopped
- ◆ 1 parsnip, scrubbed and chopped
- 6 garlic cloves, sliced
- 1 bay leaf
- 1 teaspoon salt
- ¼ teaspoon whole black peppercorns
- 8 cups water

1 Combine all ingredients in a stockpot and bring to boil over high heat. Reduce heat; skim off any foam that rises to top. Simmer, with pot partially covered, about 40 minutes.

2 Line colander with paper towel or double layer of cheesecloth; place over large bowl. Strain stock through colander, pressing solids with wooden spoon to extract juices; discard solids. Use stock immediately or transfer to 1-cup containers and let cool. Cover and refrigerate up to 3 days or freeze up to 3 months.

PER SERVING (1 cup): 12 Cal, 0 g Fat, 0 g Sat Fat, 0 g Trans Fat, 0 mg Chol, 418 mg Sod, 3 g Carb, 0 g Fib, 0 g Prot, 6 mg Calc.

IN THE KITCHEN

Use this stock to replace store-bought vegetable broth in vegetarian soups and stews. This recipe works with the Simply Filling technique.

HOW TO...
Measure Wet Ingredients

1

Place a glass measure (1-, 2-, or 4-cup) on a level work surface and add the desired amount of liquid. Bend down to check the accuracy of the measure at eye level.

2

Check the amount from above if you have an angled measuring cup.

Beef Stock (1 POINTS VALUE)

level	technique	prep	cook	serves
Basic	Simmer pg. 22	15 min	2 hr 15 min	8

- 2 teaspoons canola oil
- 4 pounds meaty beef soup bones
- 12 cups water
- ♦ 1 large onion, chopped
- ♦ 1 carrot, chopped
- ♦ 1 celery stalk, with leaves, chopped
- 6 sprigs parsley
- 1 bay leaf
- 1 teaspoon salt
- ¼ teaspoon whole black peppercorns

1 Heat 1 teaspoon of oil in stockpot over medium-high heat. Add half of bones; cook, turning often, until browned on all sides, about 5 minutes. Transfer to plate. Repeat with remaining 1 teaspoon oil and half of bones. Return browned bones to stockpot.

2 Add water, onion, carrot, celery, parsley, bay leaf, salt, and peppercorns and bring to boil. Reduce heat and skim off any foam that rises to top. Simmer, partially covered, about 2 hours.

3 Line colander with paper towel or double layer of cheesecloth; place over large bowl. Strain stock through colander, pressing solids with wooden spoon to extract juices; discard solids. Refrigerate stock until fat rises to surface; scrape off and discard fat. Use stock immediately or transfer to 1-cup containers, cover, and refrigerate up to 3 days or freeze up to 3 months.

PER SERVING (1 cup): 33 Cal, 1 g Fat, 0 g Sat Fat, 0 g Trans Fat, 0 mg Chol, 368 mg Sod, 3 g Carb, 0 g Fib, 5 g Prot, 10 mg Calc.

IN THE KITCHEN

For the best-ever pot roast and chili, use this stock instead of canned beef broth or water called for in the recipe. You can also use it to make gravies, soups, and stews. This recipe works with the Simply Filling technique.

Chicken Stock ①

level	technique	prep	cook	serves
Basic	Simmer pg. 22	15 min	2 hr 10 min	8

- 2 teaspoons canola oil
- ♦ 1 large onion, chopped
- ♦ 1 carrot, chopped
- ♦ 1 celery stalk, with leaves, chopped
- 12 cups water
- 3 pounds chicken wings or backs
- 6 sprigs parsley
- 1 teaspoon salt
- 1 bay leaf
- 1 sprig fresh thyme or $\frac{1}{2}$ teaspoon dried thyme

1 Heat oil in stockpot over medium-high heat. Add onion, carrot, and celery; cook, stirring frequently, until softened, 5 minutes. Add water, chicken, parsley, salt, bay leaf, and thyme; bring to boil. Reduce heat and skim off any foam that rises to the top. Simmer, partially covered, about 2 hours.

2 Line colander with paper towel or double layer of cheesecloth; place over large bowl. Strain stock through colander, pressing solids with wooden spoon to extract juices; discard solids. Refrigerate stock until fat rises to surface; scrape off and discard fat. Use stock immediately or transfer to 1-cup containers and let cool. Cover and refrigerate up to 3 days or freeze up to 3 months.

PER SERVING (1 cup): 38 Cal, 1 g Fat, 0 g Sat Fat, 0 g Trans Fat, 0 mg Chol, 367 mg Sod, 3 g Carb, 0 g Fib, 5 g Prot, 10 mg Calc.

IN THE KITCHEN

To make a delicious difference in flavor, use this homemade stock to replace the water when you cook rice, couscous, or bulgur. Use it instead of canned broth when you make chicken pot pie, chicken soup, gravies, or pan sauces. This recipe works with the Simply Filling technique.

INGREDIENTS
FOR CHICKEN STOCK

Homemade Marinara Sauce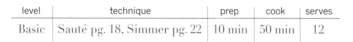

level	technique	prep	cook	serves
Basic	Sauté pg. 18, Simmer pg. 22	10 min	50 min	12

 1 tablespoon olive oil
♦ 2 celery stalks, diced
♦ 2 carrots, diced
♦ 1 large onion, diced
 4 garlic cloves, minced
♦ 2 (28-ounce) cans diced tomatoes
 2 tablespoons chopped fresh basil
   or 2 teaspoons dried
 1 teaspoon salt
 ½ teaspoon black pepper
 Pinch red pepper flakes

1 Heat oil in large Dutch oven over medium heat. Add celery, carrots, and onion; cook, stirring occasionally, until vegetables are tender, 8 minutes. Add garlic; cook, stirring constantly, until fragrant, 30 seconds.

2 Meanwhile, place 1 can of tomatoes in food processor; process until smooth. Add both cans of tomatoes, basil, salt, black pepper, and pepper flakes to pot; bring to boil. Reduce heat and simmer, uncovered, until sauce is thickened, about 35 minutes. Use sauce immediately or transfer to 1-cup containers and let cool. Cover and refrigerate up to 3 days or freeze up to 3 months.

PER SERVING (½ cup): 45 Cal, 1 g Fat, 0 g Sat Fat, 0 g Trans Fat, 0 mg Chol, 399 mg Sod, 8 g Carb, 2 g Fib, 1 g Prot, 53 mg Calc.

IN THE KITCHEN

Most purchased marinara sauces contain high amounts of added sodium and sugar. Make this version and you'll have a more healthful and delicious sauce to use in lasagna and other pasta dishes. This recipe works with the Simply Filling technique.

Asian Lime Vinaigrette ①

level	prep	cook	serves
Basic	5 min	none	8

¼ teaspoon salt

1 small garlic clove, minced

¼ cup rice vinegar

2 tablespoons lime juice

♦ 2 tablespoons Vegetable Stock (page 30) or store-bought reduced sodium vegetable broth

2 tablespoons canola oil

1 tablespoon reduced-sodium soy sauce

1 teaspoon sugar

1 On cutting board, sprinkle salt over garlic. Mash to a paste with flat side of heavy knife.

2 Combine mashed garlic with remaining ingredients in small jar with tight-fitting lid; shake well. Use immediately or refrigerate up to 1 week.

PER SERVING (1½ tablespoons): 36 Cal, 3 g Fat, 0 g Sat Fat, 0 g Trans Fat, 0 mg Chol, 146 mg Sod, 1 g Carb, 0 g Fib, 0 g Prot, 2 mg Calc.

IN THE KITCHEN

Serve this dressing over any vegetable or pasta salad where you want some Asian-inspired flavor. It also makes a perfect marinade for scallops, shrimp, salmon, and skinless chicken.

CLOCKWISE FROM LEFT:
RED WINE–SHALLOT VINAIGRETTE,
ASIAN LIME VINAIGRETTE,
BUTTERMILK-HERB DRESSING, AND
CREAMY BALSAMIC DRESSING

Red Wine–Shallot Vinaigrette

level	prep	cook	serves
Basic	5 min	none	8

- ⅓ cup minced shallots
- ¼ cup red-wine vinegar
- ♦ 2 tablespoons Vegetable Stock (page 30) or store-bought reduced-sodium vegetable broth
- 2 tablespoons extra-virgin olive oil
- 1 tablespoon honey mustard
- ¼ teaspoon salt
- ¼ teaspoon black pepper

Combine all ingredients in small jar with tight-fitting lid; shake well. Use immediately or refrigerate up to 1 week.

PER SERVING (1½ tablespoons): 41 Cal, 4 g Fat, 0 g Sat Fat, 0 g Trans Fat, 0 mg Chol, 91 mg Sod, 2 g Carb, 0 g Fib, 0 g Prot, 5 mg Calc.

IN THE KITCHEN

This dressing will wake up your usual salads with fresh flavor. Use it on any tossed green salad or pasta salad, or as a marinade for skinless chicken or shrimp.

Buttermilk-Herb Dressing ①

level	prep	cook	serves
Basic	5 min	none	8

- ⅔ cup low-fat buttermilk
- ⅓ cup fresh flat-leaf parsley leaves
- ¼ cup fresh tarragon leaves
- ◆ 2 scallions, thinly sliced
- 2½ tablespoons lemon juice
- 2 tablespoons olive oil
- ¼ teaspoon salt
- ¼ teaspoon black pepper

Combine all ingredients in blender; process until smooth. Cover and refrigerate at least 2 hours or up to 3 days. Stir before serving.

PER SERVING (2 tablespoons): 43 Cal, 4 g Fat, 1 g Sat Fat, 0 g Trans Fat, 1 mg Chol, 98 mg Sod, 2 g Carb, 0 g Fib, 1 g Prot, 36 mg Calc.

IN THE KITCHEN

Serve this creamy ranch-style dressing over salad greens or use it as a dip for fresh vegetables. If you don't like tarragon, make the recipe with fresh dill or basil instead.

Creamy Balsamic Dressing

(1 POINTS VALUE)

level	prep	cook	serves
Basic	5 min	none	10

- ¾ cup plain low-fat yogurt
- ½ cup chopped shallots
- 2½ tablespoons balsamic vinegar
- 2 tablespoons olive oil
- 1 tablespoon lemon juice
- ¼ teaspoon dried oregano
- ¼ teaspoon salt
- ¼ teaspoon black pepper

Combine all ingredients in blender; process until smooth. Cover and refrigerate at least 2 hours or up to 3 days. Stir before serving.

PER SERVING (2 tablespoons): 45 Cal, 3 g Fat, 1 g Sat Fat, 0 g Trans Fat, 1 mg Chol, 74 mg Sod, 3 g Carb, 0 g Fib, 1 g Prot, 39 mg Calc.

IN THE KITCHEN

Drizzle this creamy Italian dressing over mixed green salads, use it to make pasta salads, or serve it over a grilled chicken or shrimp salad.

10 Herbs and Spices Every Kitchen Needs

With these herbs and spices on your shelf, you'll have the basics you need for making most dishes. Expand the list according to what types of foods you cook most. Dried herbs and ground spices will stay fresh in a cool, dark place for 1 year.

- Basil
- Chili powder
- Cinnamon
- Cloves
- Cumin
- Ginger
- Nutmeg
- Oregano
- Paprika
- Peppercorns

Go-with-Everything Pico de Gallo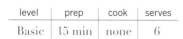

level	prep	cook	serves
Basic	15 min	none	6

- ♦ 1 pound plum tomatoes (about 6) chopped
- ♦ 1 cup chopped onion
- ½ cup chopped fresh cilantro
- 2 tablespoons lime juice
- ♦ 1 jalapeño pepper, seeded and minced
- ½ teaspoon salt
- ¼ teaspoon black pepper

Stir together all ingredients in large bowl. Cover and chill at least 30 minutes or up to 4 hours. Stir before serving.

PER SERVING (⅓ cup): 25 Cal, 0 g Fat, 0 g Sat Fat, 0 g Trans Fat, 0 mg Chol, 203 mg Sod, 6 g Carb, 1 g Fib, 1 g Prot, 15 mg Calc.

IN THE KITCHEN

Serve this garden fresh salsa with tacos or tostadas, or use it as a topping for grilled shrimp, salmon, or skinless chicken breast. **This recipe works with the** Simply Filling **technique.**

CHICKEN AND GOAT CHEESE
QUESADILLAS, PAGE 51,
AND GO-WITH-EVERYTHING
PICO DE GALLO

Spinach-Basil Pesto Sauce

(1 POINTS VALUE)

level	technique	prep	cook	serves
Basic	Boil pg. 22	10 min	5 min	8

- ◆ 2 cups packed spinach leaves
- 3 cups packed fresh basil leaves
- 2 tablespoons pine nuts, toasted
- 2 tablespoons grated Parmesan cheese
- 2 garlic cloves, chopped
- ½ teaspoon salt
- ¼ teaspoon black pepper
- ◆ ¼ cup Vegetable Stock (page 30) or store-bought reduced-sodium vegetable broth
- 1½ tablespoons olive oil

1 Bring small pot of water to boil. Add spinach and cook until wilted, about 1 minute. Drain in colander and rinse under cold running water. Squeeze out excess water and place in food processor.

2 Add basil, pine nuts, Parmesan, garlic, salt, and pepper; pulse until coarsely chopped. Add broth and oil; process until smooth. Use immediately or cover and refrigerate up to 5 days or freeze up to 3 months.

PER SERVING (2 tablespoons): 51 Cal, 5 g Fat, 1 g Sat Fat, 0 g Trans Fat, 1 mg Chol, 192 mg Sod, 1 g Carb, 1 g Fib, 2 g Prot, 59 mg Calc.

IN THE KITCHEN

Toss this pesto with hot cooked pasta, swirl it into vegetable soup, or drizzle it over a platter of sliced tomatoes.

HOW TO...
Peel Garlic

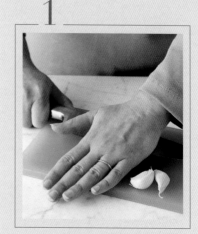

Place a garlic clove on a cutting board and cover with the broad side of a cook's knife. Press down firmly on the side of the knife to crush the clove.

Remove the split skin from the clove. Slice, chop, or mince the garlic as directed in the recipe.

No-Cook Raspberry Sauce ①

level	prep	cook	serves
Basic	10 min	none	8

- ◆ 2 cups fresh or thawed frozen raspberries
- ½ cup confectioners' sugar
- 1 tablespoon lemon juice
- 1 teaspoon orange-flavored liqueur, such as Grand Marnier (optional)

Puree all ingredients in food processor until smooth. Push puree through a strainer; discard seeds. Cover and refrigerate up to 1 week.

PER SERVING (2 tablespoons): 46 Cal, 0 g Fat, 0 g Sat Fat, 0 g Trans Fat, 0 mg Chol, 1 mg Sod, 11 g Carb, 1 g Fib, 0 g Prot, 8 mg Calc.

IN THE KITCHEN

Drizzle this sauce over store-bought angel food cake, fat-free vanilla frozen yogurt, or fresh sliced melon.

Rich Chocolate Sauce (2) POINTS VALUE

level	technique	prep	cook	serves
Basic	Simmer pg. 22	5 min	5 min	6

- ½ cup fat-free milk
- ⅓ cup sugar
- ¼ cup unsweetened cocoa powder
- Pinch salt
- 1 tablespoon semisweet chocolate chips
- 2 teaspoons unsalted butter
- ½ teaspoon vanilla extract

1 Whisk together milk, sugar, cocoa, and salt in small heavy-bottomed saucepan. Set over medium heat; bring just to simmer, whisking frequently.

2 Remove from heat; add chocolate chips, butter, and vanilla and whisk until smooth. Use immediately, or cool to room temperature, cover, and refrigerate up to 1 week. Stir well to serve chilled or gently reheat.

PER SERVING (about 2 tablespoons): 78 Cal, 2 g Fat, 1 g Sat Fat, 0 g Trans Fat, 4 mg Chol, 57 mg Sod, 15 g Carb, 1 g Fib, 1 g Prot, 31 mg Calc.

◆ FILLING EXTRA

Serve this sauce over 1½ cups fresh raspberries or strawberries (either option will increase the **POINTS** value by *1*).

Creamy Custard Sauce ①

level	technique	prep	cook	serves
Basic	Simmer pg. 22	5 min	5 min	6

1   cup low-fat (1%) milk
♦ ½   cup fat-free egg substitute
¼   cup sugar
Pinch salt
½   teaspoon vanilla extract

1 Whisk together milk, egg substitute, sugar, and salt in small saucepan, then set over medium-high heat. Cook, stirring constantly, until mixture thickens and coats back of spoon, about 4 minutes (do not let boil or mixture may curdle).

2 Immediately pour custard through fine-mesh sieve set over medium bowl; stir in vanilla. Press wax paper directly onto custard to prevent skin from forming. Serve warm, or transfer to covered container and refrigerate up to 4 days. Serve chilled, or gently reheat to serve warm.

PER SERVING (generous ¼ cup): 59 Cal, 0 g Fat, 0 g Sat Fat, 0 g Trans Fat, 2 mg Chol, 69 mg Sod, 11 g Carb, 0 g Fib, 3 g Prot, 50 mg Calc.

CHAPTER 2

Nibbles & Noshes

Whether you're looking for a flavorful dip for fresh veggies, a few easy appetizers to serve at a party, or a light soup or salad to whet the appetite before dinner, these great-tasting starters will get you off to a scrumptious beginning. Each recipe has a **POINTS** value of *3* or less, so go ahead and indulge!

Grilled Beef, Spinach, and Feta Bruschetta (3 POINTS VALUE)

level	technique	prep	cook	serves
Basic	Grill pg. 26	20 min	15 min	12

- ♦ 1 (1-pound) beef tenderloin, trimmed
- ½ teaspoon salt
- ¼ teaspoon black pepper
- 1 (20-inch) whole wheat baguette
- 2 tablespoons horseradish sauce
- 1 cup lightly packed baby spinach
- ¼ cup crumbled feta cheese
- ♦ 2 tablespoons minced scallions

1 Spray grill rack with nonstick spray. Preheat grill to medium-high or prepare medium-high fire.

2 Sprinkle tenderloin with salt and pepper. Place on grill rack and grill, turning once, until instant-read thermometer inserted into center registers 145°F for medium, about 12 minutes. Transfer to cutting board and let stand 5 minutes. Slice tenderloin across grain into 24 thin slices.

3 Cut baguette on diagonal into 24 (½-inch) slices; lightly spray with nonstick spray. Place slices on grill rack and grill until well marked, about 1 minute on each side. Spread baguette slices evenly with horseradish sauce and top with spinach, beef, and feta. Sprinkle evenly with scallions and arrange on platter.

PER SERVING (2 bruschetta): 129 Cal, 4 g Fat, 2 g Sat Fat, 0 g Trans Fat, 20 mg Chol, 271 mg Sod, 11 g Carb, 2 g Fib, 12 g Prot, 50 mg Calc.

IN THE KITCHEN

You can make the bruschetta with a 1-pound pork tenderloin instead of the beef. To prepare the pork, grill it until an instant-read thermometer inserted in the center registers 160°F, about 25 minutes.

GRILLED BEEF, SPINACH, AND FETA BRUSCHETTA AND SHRIMP COCKTAIL WITH SMOKY TOMATO SALSA, PAGE 53

Ginger-Soy Glazed Chicken Skewers (3 POINTS VALUE)

level	technique	prep	cook	serves
Basic	Broil pg. 25	10 min	15 min	6

3	tablespoons reduced-sodium soy sauce
2	tablespoons rice vinegar
2	tablespoons orange juice
2	tablespoons grated peeled fresh ginger
1	tablespoon sugar
♦ 1	pound skinless boneless chicken breast, cut into 2-inch chunks
♦ 1	scallion, thinly sliced

1 Spray broiler rack with nonstick spray. Preheat broiler.

2 To make basting sauce, combine soy sauce, vinegar, orange juice, ginger, and sugar in small saucepan; bring to boil over medium-high heat. Cook until sauce is reduced to $1/3$ cup, about 6 minutes.

3 Meanwhile, thread chicken onto 6 (8-inch) metal skewers. Arrange skewers on broiler rack; brush with half of sauce. Broil 4 inches from heat, turning once and basting with remaining sauce, until chicken is cooked through, 8–10 minutes. Sprinkle chicken with scallion. Serve hot or warm.

PER SERVING (1 chicken skewer): 117 Cal, 3 g Fat, 1 g Sat Fat, 0 g Trans Fat, 47 mg Chol, 310 mg Sod, 5 g Carb, 0 g Fib, 18 g Prot, 13 mg Calc.

♦ FILLING EXTRA

Thread 1 red onion, quartered and separated into slices and 1 green bell pepper, cut into 1-inch pieces onto the skewers with the chicken.

Saved by a Snack

For most, eating three meals a day isn't enough to keep your energy going all day. But you want to make sure you're making smart snacking decisions by pinpointing what food you're really craving.

If You're *Really* Hungry….
Get satisfied with air-popped popcorn, baby carrots and black bean dip, a cup of berries, or an apple.

If You're in a 3 p.m. Slump...
Reach for a high-energy snack, such as a smoothie made with $1/2$ cup fat-free yogurt and a small banana, strawberries dipped in dark chocolate, or hummus with bell pepper strips.

If You're Seeking a Sweet...
Try a frozen fruit bar, a few clusters of frozen grapes, or a few hard candies. When it's cold outside, enjoy a mug of fat-free hot chocolate topped with a few mini marshmallows.

If You're Working Late...
Reach for a high-fiber snack and a bit of cheese to tide you over. Think whole-grain crackers and a smear of peanut butter or a wedge of light cheese and a few apple slices. Or enjoy 12 or so walnuts or almonds along with a little dried fruit, such as cranberries or cherries.

If You're Bored...
Opt for a snack that takes time to prepare or to eat, such as peanuts in the shell, a fruit that requires some prep work, such as pineapple, or a treat that takes a bit of time to compose, such as a sundae made with plain low-fat yogurt, chopped fresh fruit, and a sprinkling of whole-grain cereal.

Chicken and Goat Cheese Quesadillas (3 POINTS VALUE)

level	technique	prep	cook	serves
Basic	Sauté pg. 18	15 min	30 min	8

- 2 teaspoons canola oil
- ♦ 1 (10-ounce) package white mushrooms, thinly sliced
- ¼ teaspoon salt
- ♦ 1½ cups shredded cooked chicken breast
- 3 ounces reduced-fat soft (mild) goat cheese, crumbled
- ♦ 1 jalapeño pepper, seeded and minced
- 4 (8-inch) whole wheat tortillas
- ♦ ½ cup Go-with-Everything Pico de Gallo (page 40)
  or store-bought salsa

1 Heat oil in large nonstick skillet over medium-high heat. Add mushrooms and salt and cook, stirring occasionally, until tender, about 8 minutes.

2 Sprinkle one quarter of mushrooms, chicken, goat cheese, and jalapeño on half of each tortilla. Fold unfilled half of each tortilla over filling, pressing down lightly.

3 Wipe out skillet and spray with nonstick spray; set over medium heat. Cook quesadillas, one at a time, until crisp and heated through, about 3 minutes on each side. Cut each quesadilla into 4 wedges; arrange on platter. Serve with pico de gallo.

PER SERVING (2 quesadilla wedges and 1 tablespoon pico de gallo): 140 Cal, 5 g Fat, 2 g Sat Fat, 0 g Trans Fat, 26 mg Chol, 309 mg Sod, 12 g Carb, 2 g Fib, 13 g Prot, 27 mg Calc.

◈ FILLING EXTRA

Cook 3 cups baby spinach or chopped fresh spinach along with the mushrooms. Add the spinach during the last 2 minutes of cooking.

Tuna and White Bean Crostini ③

level	technique	prep	cook	serves
Basic	Pan Sear pg. 20	20 min	5 min	8

- ◆ 1 (15½-ounce) can cannellini (white kidney) beans, rinsed and drained
- 1 tablespoon chopped fresh chives
- 1 tablespoon lemon juice
- 3 teaspoons olive oil
- 1 garlic clove, minced
- ◆ 1 (½-pound) tuna steak, about 1 inch thick
- ¼ teaspoon salt
- ⅛ teaspoon black pepper
- 1 (8-ounce) whole wheat baguette, cut on the diagonal into 16 slices, toasted
- ◆ 16 thin slices English (seedless) cucumber

1 Combine beans, chives, lemon juice, 2 teaspoons of oil, and garlic in a medium bowl; coarsely mash with fork.

2 Heat remaining 1 teaspoon oil in medium skillet over medium-high heat. Sprinkle tuna with salt and pepper. Add tuna; cook 2–3 minutes on each side for medium-rare or until desired doneness. Transfer tuna to cutting board; let stand about 5 minutes.

3 Cut tuna into 16 slices. Spread each baguette slice with about 1 tablespoon of bean mixture; top each with 1 slice cucumber, then with 1 slice tuna.

PER SERVING (2 crostini): 176 Cal, 4 g Fat, 1 g Sat Fat, 0 g Trans Fat, 17 mg Chol, 338 mg Sod, 22 g Carb, 4 g Fib, 13 g Prot, 70 mg Calc.

IN THE KITCHEN

When you serve cucumbers with the skin on, always choose the English (seedless) variety. They have a thinner skin and no wax coating on the outside as regular cucumbers do.

Shrimp Cocktail with Smoky Tomato Salsa (2 POINTS VALUE)

level	technique	prep	cook	serves
Basic	Boil pg. 22	20 min	10 min	6

- ♦ 1½ pounds large unpeeled shrimp
- ♦ 1 pound tomatoes, seeded and chopped
- ♦ ¼ cup diced red onion
- 2 tablespoons chopped fresh cilantro
- 2 teaspoons lime juice
- 1½ teaspoons minced chipotle en adobo
- 1½ teaspoons canola oil
- 1 small garlic clove, minced
- ⅛ teaspoon salt
- 6 lime wedges

1 Bring large pot of water to boil. Add shrimp and cook, stirring frequently, until just opaque in center, about 3 minutes. Drain in colander. Rinse shrimp under cold running water and drain. Peel and devein shrimp leaving tails on, if desired. Pat dry on paper towels.

2. Stir together tomatoes, onion, cilantro, lime juice, chipotle en adobo, oil, garlic, and salt in medium bowl.

3 Evenly divide shrimp and arrange on 6 plates; spoon ¼ cup of salsa onto each plate. Serve with lime wedges.

PER SERVING (1 shrimp cocktail): 83 Cal, 2 g Fat, 0 g Sat Fat, 0 g Trans Fat, 107 mg Chol, 186 mg Sod, 5 g Carb, 1 g Fib, 12 g Prot, 34 mg Calc.

♦ FILLING EXTRA

Turn the shrimp and salsa into a light lunch by serving them on a bed of baby spinach surrounded with cucumber slices and red bell pepper strips. This recipe works with the Simply Filling technique.

5 Snacks under 1 POINTS value

Here are some tasty and good-for-you way to stave off hunger for a **POINTS** value of only **1**.

1 heat a cup of instant chicken-vegetable soup

2 mash ¼ cup fresh raspberries in a small bowl; stir in ½ cup plain fat-free yogurt

3 dip 6 medium baby carrots into ½ cup salsa

4 wrap 2 medium dill pickles with 2 (1-ounce) slices of lean turkey breast

5 mix a sugar-free vanilla pudding snack cup with ½ cup solid pack pumpkin

Moroccan Carrot Dip with Toasted Pita Triangles ②

level	technique	prep	cook	serves
Basic	Broil pg. 25, Bake pg. 27	10 min	25 min	6

- 3 (6-inch) whole wheat pita breads, cut into 8 wedges each
- 1 teaspoon salt
- ♦ 1 pound carrots, cut into 1-inch pieces
- 1 tablespoon olive oil
- 1 small garlic clove, minced
- 1½ teaspoons lemon juice
- 1 teaspoon paprika
- ½ teaspoon ground cumin
- ¼ teaspoon cinnamon
- ¼ teaspoon ground coriander
- Pinch cayenne
- 1 tablespoon chopped fresh flat-leaf parsley

1 Preheat oven to 400°F.

2 Split each pita into 2 rounds; lightly coat both sides of each round with nonstick spray. Sprinkle one side of the rounds evenly with ½ teaspoon of salt. Cut each round into 8 wedges; arrange wedges in single layer on large baking sheet. Bake until crisp and lightly toasted, 6–7 minutes. Transfer to wire rack to cool.

3 Meanwhile, combine carrots and enough water to cover in large saucepan and bring to boil. Cook until fork-tender, about 20 minutes. Drain in colander and let cool 5 minutes.

4 Put carrots, oil, garlic, lemon juice, paprika, cumin, cinnamon, coriander, cayenne, and remaining ½ teaspoon salt in food processor and process until smooth. Transfer to serving bowl; sprinkle with parsley. Serve warm or at room temperature with pita triangles.

PER SERVING (¼ cup dip with 8 pita triangles): 142 Cal, 3 g Fat, 0 g Sat Fat, 0 g Trans Fat, 0 mg Chol, 403 mg Sod, 26 g Carb, 5 g Fib, 4 g Prot, 29 mg Calc.

IN THE KITCHEN

Use 1 pound of baby carrots and you won't have to peel or cut up the carrots.

Pineapple-Poblano Salsa (0 POINTS VALUE)

level	technique	prep	cook	serves
Basic	Broil pg. 25	15 min	5 min	8

- ♦ 1 poblano pepper
- ♦ 2 cups diced, peeled, and cored fresh pineapple
- ♦ ¼ cup diced red onion
-    1 garlic clove, minced
-    2 tablespoons chopped fresh cilantro
-    1 tablespoon lime juice
-    ½ teaspoon salt

1 Preheat broiler. Place poblano on baking sheet and broil 5 inches from heat, turning occasionally, until blackened on all sides, about 4 minutes. Place poblano in paper bag and fold closed. Let steam 10 minutes.

2 Meanwhile, combine pineapple, onion, garlic, cilantro, lime juice, and salt in a medium bowl. When cool enough to handle, peel poblano, discard seeds, and chop. Add poblano to pineapple mixture; stir gently. Serve at once or store, covered, in refrigerator up to 2 days.

PER SERVING (⅓ cup): 28 Cal, 0 g Fat, 0 g Sat Fat, 0 g Trans Fat, 0 mg Chol, 147 mg Sod, 7 g Carb, 1 g Fib, 1 g Prot, 9 mg Calc.

◆ FILLING EXTRA

Red, yellow, and green bell pepper strips make colorful dippers for this salsa. This recipe works with the Simply Filling technique.

**MIXED GREEN SALAD
WITH AVOCADO AND
ROASTED CORN**

Mixed Green Salad with Avocado and Roasted Corn (2) POINTS VALUE

level	technique	prep	cook	serves
Basic	Roast pg. 24	15 min	25 min	4

- ♦ 1 cup fresh or thawed frozen corn kernels
-   3 tablespoons fresh lime juice
-   1 teaspoon olive oil
-   ½ teaspoon salt
-   ½ teaspoon black pepper
- ♦ 1 small head Bibb lettuce, torn into bite-size pieces
- ♦ ½ small head romaine, torn into bite-size pieces
- ♦ ½ Hass avocado, pitted, peeled, and chopped
- ♦ 1 small red onion, thinly sliced
- ♦ 1 cup cherry tomatoes, halved

1 Preheat oven to 425°F. Spray large rimmed baking sheet with nonstick spray.

2 Spread corn on baking sheet and roast, stirring twice, until lightly browned, 25 minutes. Let cool slightly.

3 Whisk together lime juice, oil, salt, and pepper in a large bowl. Add Bibb, romaine, avocado, onion, tomatoes, and corn and toss to coat.

PER SERVING (1½ cups): 103 Cal, 4 g Fat, 1 g Sat Fat, 0 g Trans Fat, 0 mg Chol, 310 mg Sod, 16 g Carb, 5 g Fib, 3 g Prot, 50 mg Calc.

♦ FILLING EXTRA

To add more protein and fiber to this salad, toss in 1 cup rinsed and drained canned black beans. This recipe works with the Simply Filling technique.

Broccoli and Red Apple Salad (2 POINTS VALUE)

level	technique	prep	cook	serves
Basic	Boil pg. 22	10 min	5 min	4

- ◆ 2 cups fresh small broccoli florets
- 2 tablespoons low-fat sour cream
- 1 tablespoon apple cider vinegar
- 1 teaspoon honey
- ¼ teaspoon salt
- ⅛ teaspoon black pepper
- ◆ 1 McIntosh apple, chopped
- 2 tablespoons golden raisins
- 2 tablespoons chopped toasted walnuts

1 Bring large saucepan of lightly salted water to a boil. Add broccoli and cook just until crisp-tender, 3 minutes. Drain. Rinse under cold running water until cool and drain. Pat dry on paper towels.

2 Whisk together sour cream, vinegar, honey, salt, and pepper in medium bowl. Add broccoli, apple, and raisins; toss to coat. Serve at once or cover and refrigerate up to 4 hours. Sprinkle with walnuts just before serving.

PER SERVING (¾ cup): 90 Cal, 3 g Fat, 1 g Sat Fat, 0 g Trans Fat, 3 mg Chol, 168 mg Sod, 15 g Carb, 2 g Fib, 2 g Prot, 36 mg Calc.

◆ FILLING EXTRA

Chop 1 firm-ripe Bartlett or Bosc pear and add to the salad.

Snack Smart, Save $

It is a misconception that healthier foods always cost more. Here are 5 ways to plan ahead for snacks without going over your daily **POINTS** Target or breaking your grocery budget.

Single-serve snacks are often pricey. Make your own pre-packaged varieties. Buy large bags or boxes of pretzels, cereal, or baked chips and portion them out into snack-size plastic bags or containers.

Create healthier (and cheaper) versions of your childhood favorites. Buy pudding in powdered form and mix it with fat-free milk. Make your own potato "chips" (slice potatoes, coat with nonstick spray, sprinkle with salt, and bake). Freeze orange or cranberry juice in small paper cups for homemade popsicles.

Choose in-season fruits and vegetables. They are more flavorful and they cost less, too. Fruits and vegetables that are deeply colored are the most healthful and those that have the most crunch are the most satisfying.

Shop smart. Look for buy-one, get-one-free specials, double-coupon days, and supermarket savings cards that offer more bang for the buck. Buying the store brand over brand names can help you spend less, too.

Focus on eating (over drinking) your calories. Whole fruits and vegetables contain more fiber, which helps you feel satisfied longer. They take longer to eat and tend to be cheaper than similar packaged drinks.

Creamy Broccoli-Lemon Soup (2 POINTS VALUE)

level	technique	prep	cook	serves
Basic	Simmer pg. 22	10 min	20 min	6

1	tablespoon unsalted butter
1	small onion, diced
3	tablespoons all-purpose flour
♦ 4	cups Chicken Stock (page 32) or store-bought reduced-sodium chicken broth
♦ 4	cups fresh broccoli florets
⅓	cup crumbled feta cheese
1	teaspoon grated lemon zest

1 Melt butter in large saucepan over medium heat. Add onion and cook, stirring occasionally, until softened, about 5 minutes. Add flour and cook, stirring constantly, about 1 minute. Gradually add stock, stirring constantly. Bring to boil, stirring occasionally.

2 Reduce heat and simmer, stirring occasionally, until mixture thickens slightly, about 2 minutes. Add broccoli and simmer, stirring occasionally, until tender, 7–8 minutes.

3 Let cool about 5 minutes. Stir in feta. Pour soup in batches into a blender; puree. Return soup to pan; stir in lemon zest. Reheat over medium heat (do not boil).

PER SERVING (generous ¾ cup): 99 Cal, 5 g Fat, 3 g Sat Fat, 0 g Trans Fat, 12 mg Chol, 353 mg Sod, 9 g Carb, 2 g Fib, 6 g Prot, 74 mg Calc.

◆ FILLING EXTRA

If you love broccoli, garnish this creamy soup with it, too. Put 3 cups small broccoli florets in a microwavable shallow dish and add 2 tablespoons water. Cover with wax paper and microwave on High until crisp-tender, about 3 minutes. Drain and spoon ½ cup of the florets into each bowl of soup.

BUTTERNUT SQUASH SOUP WITH
PEAR AND CHEESE TOASTS

Butternut Squash Soup with Pear and Cheese Toasts (2 POINTS VALUE)

level	technique	prep	cook	serves
Basic	Simmer pg. 22, Bake pg. 27	10 min	30 min	6

- ◆ 2 ripe small pears, peeled, halved, and cored
- ◆ 1 onion, chopped
-   $\frac{1}{2}$ teaspoon ground cardamom
-   $\frac{1}{2}$ teaspoon ground coriander
- ◆ 1 (2-pound) butternut squash, seeded, peeled, and cut into $\frac{1}{2}$-inch pieces
- ◆ $2\frac{1}{2}$ cups Chicken Stock (page 32) or store-bought reduced-sodium chicken broth
-   1 tablespoon lemon juice
-   $\frac{1}{2}$ teaspoon salt
-   3 slices pumpernickel bread, crusts removed
-   $1\frac{1}{2}$ tablespoons crumbled blue cheese, at room temperature

1 Reserve 1 pear half for toasts; coarsely chop remaining pears.

2 Spray large nonstick saucepan with nonstick spray; set over medium heat. Add onion, cardamom, and coriander. Cook, stirring frequently, until onion is softened, about 5 minutes. Add squash, stock, and chopped pear; bring to boil. Reduce heat and simmer, covered, until squash is tender, about 20 minutes.

3 Let cool about 5 minutes. Pour soup in batches into blender and puree. Return soup to pan; stir in lemon juice and salt. Reheat over medium heat.

4 Meanwhile, to make toasts, preheat oven to 350°F. Cut each bread slice in half diagonally; place on baking sheet. Bake, turning once, until lightly toasted, 10 minutes.

5 Cut 12 slices from reserved pear half and arrange 2 slices on each piece of bread; top evenly with cheese. Return to oven until cheese melts slightly, about 1 minute. Spoon soup evenly into 6 bowls and serve with toasts.

PER SERVING (1 cup soup with 1 toast): 139 Cal, 2 g Fat, 1 g Sat Fat, 0 g Trans Fat, 2 mg Chol, 471 mg Sod, 29 g Carb, 4 g Fib, 5 g Prot, 81 mg Calc.

◆ FILLING EXTRA

For a creamy finish, top each serving of soup with 1 tablespoon fat-free plain yogurt.

CHAPTER 3

Breakfasts & Brunches

You'll never want to skip breakfast once you've tried these tempting recipes. Here you'll find make-ahead breakfasts such as tender muffins and crunchy granola, an eat-on-the-go tortilla-wrapped omelette, and for lazy weekend mornings, French toast and fresh apple coffeecake.

Spinach and Mushroom Frittata with Goat Cheese

4 POINTS VALUE

level	technique	prep	cook	serves
Basic	Sauté pg. 18, Broil pg. 25	10 min	25 min	4

- ♦ 4 large eggs
- ♦ 4 large egg whites
- ½ teaspoon salt
- ¼ teaspoon black pepper
- ♦ 1 (8-ounce) container sliced mushrooms
- ♦ 1 (6-ounce) bag baby spinach
- ½ cup fat-free garlic-onion croutons
- ♦ 2 plum tomatoes, sliced
- 2 ounces goat cheese, crumbled

1 Whisk together eggs, egg whites, ¼ teaspoon salt, and pepper in large bowl.

2 Spray 10-inch nonstick ovenproof skillet with nonstick spray and set over medium heat. Add mushrooms and remaining ¼ teaspoon salt and cook, stirring occasionally, until lightly browned and most of liquid evaporates, about 8 minutes. Add spinach, in batches if necessary, and cook, stirring constantly, until wilted and most of liquid evaporates, about 2 minutes.

3 Preheat broiler.

4 Sprinkle vegetable mixture with croutons; pour egg mixture evenly over croutons. Reduce heat and cook until eggs are set, 7–8 minutes (but do not stir).

5 Arrange tomato slices on top of eggs; sprinkle evenly with cheese. Place skillet under broiler and broil frittata 5 inches from heat until top is lightly browned, about 2 minutes. Cut into 4 wedges.

PER SERVING (1 wedge): 184 Cal, 9 g Fat, 4 g Sat Fat, 0 g Trans Fat, 219 mg Chol, 606 mg Sod, 10 g Carb, 2 g Fib, 17 g Prot, 107 mg Calc.

♦ FILLING EXTRA

Cook 1 small thinly sliced red onion with the mushrooms in step 2.

Wrap-and-Go Sausage and Pepper Omelette

(7 POINTS VALUE)

level	technique	prep	cook	serves
Basic	Sauté pg. 18	10 min	10 min	1

  2 frozen fully-cooked turkey breakfast sausage links, thawed and sliced (1½ ounces)

♦ ¼ cup diced onion

♦ ¼ cup diced green bell pepper

♦ 1 large egg

♦ 1 large egg white

  ⅛ teaspoon black pepper

Pinch salt

♦ 3 tablespoons shredded fat-free mozzarella cheese

  1 (8-inch) whole-grain tortilla, warmed

1 Spray medium nonstick skillet with nonstick spray and set over medium heat. Add sausage, onion, and bell pepper to skillet and cook, stirring occasionally, until vegetables are tender, about 5 minutes.

2 Meanwhile, whisk together egg, egg white, pepper, and salt in small bowl. Pour evenly over sausage mixture. Reduce heat to medium-low; cover and cook until eggs are just set on top, about 2 minutes. Sprinkle with cheese; cover and cook until cheese melts, about 1 minute. With spatula, slide omelette onto tortilla. Roll up and cut in half.

PER SERVING (1 wrap): 331 Cal, 11 g Fat, 3 g Sat Fat, 0 g Trans Fat, 255 mg Chol, 1,128 mg Sod, 27 g Carb, 4 g Fib, 30 g Prot, 247 mg Calc.

◈ FILLING EXTRA

Sprinkle the top of the omelette with 1 small chopped tomato before rolling it up.

HOW TO...
Chop an Onion

1

With a sharp knife, cut the onion in half vertically, from top to root end. Peel and place the flat sides down on a cutting board. Make two or three horizontal cuts toward the root end.

2

Make vertical cuts, ¼ inch apart, keeping the root end intact. Then make perpendicular cuts, chopping the onion into uniform size cubes.

Eggs Poached in Spicy Tomato-Cilantro Sauce

level	technique	prep	cook	serves
Basic	Sauté pg. 18, Simmer pg. 22	10 min	25 min	4

- ½ teaspoon olive oil
- ♦ 1 onion, halved lengthwise and sliced
- ♦ 1 yellow bell pepper, thinly sliced
- ♦ 1 jalapeño pepper, seeded and minced
- 1 garlic clove, minced
- ♦ 1 (14½-ounce) can diced tomatoes
- ♦ 1 (8-ounce) can tomato sauce
- ¼ teaspoon salt
- ¼ cup chopped fresh cilantro
- ♦ 4 large eggs
- ½ cup shredded reduced-fat Mexican 4-cheese blend
- 2 whole wheat English muffins, split and toasted

1 Heat oil in medium nonstick skillet over medium heat. Add onion, bell pepper, and jalapeño and cook, stirring occasionally, until vegetables are tender, about 5 minutes. Add garlic, and cook, stirring constantly, until fragrant, 30 seconds.

2 Stir in tomatoes, tomato sauce, and salt. Reduce heat and simmer, stirring occasionally, until sauce is slightly thickened, about 10 minutes. Stir in cilantro.

3 With back of spoon, make four wells in sauce and carefully break 1 egg into each. Cover and simmer until whites are opaque and yolks are set, 5–6 minutes. Sprinkle with cheese. Cover and simmer until cheese melts, about 1 minute.

4 Place a muffin half on each of 4 plates; top each with an egg and spoon sauce evenly around muffins.

PER SERVING (1 egg with sauce and ½ muffin): 238 Cal, 10 g Fat, 4 g Sat Fat, 0 g Trans Fat, 220 mg Chol, 914 mg Sod, 26 g Carb, 5 g Fib, 14 g Prot, 249 mg Calc.

♦ FILLING EXTRA

Stir 1 cup rinsed and drained canned black beans in with the tomatoes.

HOW TO...
Chop Vegetables

To Julienne: For round or oblong vegetables (potatoes, peppers), trim a thin slice off the bottom so that the vegetable can rest firmly on a cutting board. Slice lengthwise; then stack pieces and cut into strips of equal thickness. For long, thin vegetables (zucchini, carrots), cut into 2-inch chunks; then slice the pieces lengthwise. Stack the slices a few at a time and cut into strips of equal thickness.

To Dice: Follow the technique for julienne, above; then hold the vegetable strips together and cut across to make cubes.

Sweet Potato and Ham Hash ③ POINTS VALUE

level	technique	prep	cook	serves
Basic	Sauté pg. 18	15 min	25 min	6

- ♦ 3 medium sweet potatoes (about 2 pounds)
- ♦ 1 medium onion, chopped
- ♦ 1 red bell pepper, diced
- ♦ 1 green bell pepper, diced
-   1 teaspoon Cajun seasoning
-   ¼ teaspoon salt
- ♦ 1 (¼-pound) slice reduced-sodium lean ham, trimmed and diced
- ♦ 2 scallions, thinly sliced

1 Pierce potatoes in several places with fork. Place potatoes in microwavable dish. Cover with wax paper and microwave on High until potatoes feel soft when pressed, but are not fully cooked, about 10 minutes. Carefully transfer potatoes to cutting board, cut in half lengthwise, and let cool.

2 Meanwhile, spray large nonstick skillet with nonstick spray and set over medium heat. Add onion and bell peppers and cook, stirring often, until tender and lightly browned, about 10 minutes.

3 Peel and chop potatoes and add to skillet. Stir in Cajun seasoning and salt. Cook, stirring occasionally, until potatoes are tender and golden, about 8 minutes. Stir in ham and cook to heat through, about 2 minutes. Stir in scallions and cook 1 minute.

PER SERVING (1 cup): 163 Cal, 3 g Fat, 1 g Sat Fat, 0 g Trans Fat, 21 mg Chol, 691 mg Sod, 24 g Carb, 4 g Fib, 11 g Prot, 49 mg Calc.

◊ FILLING EXTRA

Stir in 1 cup thawed frozen corn with the ham. This recipe works with the Simply Filling technique.

Baked Egg Cups with Roasted Vegetables (4 POINTS VALUE)

level	technique	prep	cook	serves
Intermediate	Roast pg. 24, Bake pg. 27	15 min	40 min	4

- ♦ 1   pound plum tomatoes, cut into 1-inch chunks
- ♦ 1   red or yellow bell pepper, cut into $3/4$-inch pieces
- ♦ 1   zucchini, quartered lengthwise and cut crosswise into $3/4$-inch chunks
- ♦ 1   onion, halved lengthwise and sliced
-    2   large garlic cloves, minced
-    $1/2$ teaspoon dried herbes de Provence or Italian seasoning
-    $1/2$ teaspoon salt
-    $1/4$ teaspoon black pepper
- ♦ 4   large eggs
-    $1/4$ cup grated Parmesan cheese

1 Preheat oven to 400°F and spray a large shallow roasting pan with nonstick spray.

2 Put tomatoes, bell pepper, zucchini, onion, garlic, herbes de Provence, salt, and pepper in pan and spray with nonstick spray; toss to coat. Roast, stirring occasionally, until vegetables are browned and crisp-tender, about 30 minutes.

3 Spray four (8- or 10-ounce) ramekins or custard cups with nonstick spray. Divide vegetables evenly among cups. Make well in center of vegetables and carefully break 1 egg into each cup. Sprinkle with Parmesan. Place cups on baking sheet and bake until eggs are just set, 20–25 minutes.

PER SERVING (1 ramekin): 175 Cal, 8 g Fat, 3 g Sat Fat, 0 g Trans Fat, 217 mg Chol, 483 mg Sod, 11 g Carb, 3 g Fib, 11 g Prot, 140 mg Calc.

IN THE KITCHEN

To make sure you don't get any egg shells in the ramekins, break each egg into a small bowl and remove any bits of shells before sliding the egg on top of the vegetables in the ramekin.

BAKED EGG CUPS WITH ROASTED VEGETABLES

Popover Pancake with Warm Berry Compote (5 POINTS VALUE)

level	technique	prep	cook	serves
Basic	Bake pg. 27, Simmer pg. 22	20 min	20 min	4

- ◆ 3 large eggs
- ◆ 1 large egg white
- ◆ ¾ cup fat-free milk
- ½ cup white whole wheat flour
- 2 tablespoons + ¼ cup sugar
- ¼ teaspoon salt
- 2 teaspoons butter
- 3 tablespoons water
- 1 tablespoon fresh lemon juice
- ◆ 1 (1-pound) container strawberries, hulled and halved
- ◆ 1 cup blueberries
- ◆ ½ cup raspberries

1 Preheat oven to 425°F. Place 10-inch ovenproof skillet in oven to heat for 5 minutes.

2 Whisk together eggs, egg white, milk, flour, 2 tablespoons sugar, and salt in large bowl until smooth.

3 Remove skillet from oven, add butter, and swirl so that butter covers skillet. Pour in batter. Bake until puffed and browned at edges, about 20 minutes.

4 Meanwhile, to make compote, stir together remaining ¼ cup sugar, water, and lemon juice in a medium saucepan. Set over medium-high heat and bring to boil, stirring until the sugar is dissolved. Reduce heat and simmer 1 minute. Add strawberries and blueberries and simmer, stirring occasionally, until fruit is warm, about 4 minutes. Gently stir in raspberries.

5 Cut pancake into 4 wedges and serve at once with compote.

PER SERVING (¼ of pancake with 1 cup compote): 284 Cal, 7 g Fat, 3 g Sat Fat, 0 g Trans Fat, 165 mg Chol, 230 mg Sod, 48 g Carb, 6 g Fib, 11 g Prot, 106 mg Calc.

IN THE KITCHEN

A cast iron skillet works best for baking the pancake but any heavy skillet will do. Serve the pancake immediately when it comes out of the oven, since it rapidly deflates as it cools.

Cranberry-Almond Granola (5 POINTS VALUE)

level	technique	prep	cook	serves
Basic	Bake pg. 27	10 min	35 min	8

- 3 cups old-fashioned rolled oats
- ¼ cup whole almonds, coarsely chopped
- ¼ cup raw sunflower seeds
- 3 tablespoons wheat germ
- ½ teaspoon cinnamon
- ¼ cup honey
- ¼ cup pure maple syrup
- ¾ cup dried cranberries

1 Preheat oven to 300°F. Spray 10 x 15-inch rimmed baking sheet with nonstick spray.

2 Stir together oats, almonds, sunflower seeds, wheat germ, and cinnamon in large bowl. Add honey and maple syrup and stir to coat. Spoon mixture onto baking sheet and spread evenly.

3 Bake, stirring occasionally, until oats and almonds are golden brown, about 35 minutes. Stir in cranberries and let cool completely. The granola can be stored in an airtight container up to 2 weeks.

PER SERVING (about ½ cup): 270 Cal, 7 g Fat, 1 g Sat Fat, 0 g Trans Fat, 0 mg Chol, 5 mg Sod, 49 g Carb, 5 g Fib, 7 g Prot, 42 mg Calc.

◆ FILLING EXTRA

Serve the granola with 1½ cups strawberries and ½ cup plain fat-free yogurt (the per-serving **POINTS** value will increase by **2**).

Don't Skip It!

Even though eating breakfast has long been linked to good health and a nutritious diet, skipping that morning meal may seem like an easy way to cut calories when trying to lose weight. Yet breakfast eaters tend to weigh less than breakfast skippers and some studies have even found that skippers can end up eating more calories through the course of the day compared to those who have an a.m. meal. If you skip breakfast, stop: you're more likely to be famished by lunch and end up eating too much.

Eating breakfast is one of the key strategies for maintaining lost pounds. It can also help to reduce hunger later in the day, as well as provide key nutrients that may enhance physical activity, another key strategy for maintaining weight loss.

The Bottom Line: Making breakfast part of your daily routine is a key strategy for long-term, sustainable weight loss. So follow this a.m. recipe for success: An ideal breakfast is a combination of protein (which slows digestion) and carbohydrates (which deliver a quick shot of energy). Here are some good choices:

- low-fat cheese and tomato slices on a whole wheat English muffin
- high-fiber cereal with fat-free or low-fat milk and dried or fresh fruit
- peanut butter and jelly on multigrain or whole wheat bread
- hard-boiled or scrambled eggs (or egg whites) with a slice of whole wheat toast
- low-fat yogurt and a grain-rich cereal bar
- a banana and a small handful of peanuts or almonds

**COCONUT FRENCH TOAST
WITH TROPICAL FRUIT**

Coconut French Toast with Tropical Fruit (5 POINTS VALUE)

level	technique	prep	cook	serves
Basic	Sauté pg. 18	25 min	15 min	8

1¼ cups light coconut milk
- 1 cup fat-free egg substitute
  4 tablespoons packed light brown sugar
  2 teaspoons vanilla extract
  8 slices whole wheat sandwich bread
  ⅓ cup flaked sweetened coconut
- 2 large bananas, halved lengthwise and sliced
- 1 mango, peeled, pitted, and diced
- ½ pineapple, peeled, cored, and diced
- ½ (1-pound) container strawberries, hulled and diced
  1 tablespoon fresh lime juice

1 Whisk together coconut milk, egg substitute, 2 tablespoons brown sugar, and vanilla in large shallow bowl or pie plate. Dip bread into egg mixture, one slice at a time, until evenly soaked. Sprinkle evenly with coconut.

2 Spray large nonstick skillet with nonstick spray; set over medium heat. Add soaked bread to skillet in batches; cook until browned, 2 minutes on each side.

3 Meanwhile, stir together remaining 2 tablespoons brown sugar, bananas, mango, pineapple, strawberries, and lime juice. Serve French toast topped with fruit.

PER SERVING (1 slice French toast with ½ cup fruit): 279 Cal, 5 g Fat, 3 g Sat Fat, 0 g Trans Fat, 0 mg Chol, 298 mg Sod, 51 g Carb, 6 g Fib, 11 g Prot, 122 mg Calc.

IN THE KITCHEN

To add a touch of sweetness, place 2 teaspoons confectioners' sugar in a fine wire mesh sieve and sprinkle evenly over the French toast slices just before serving.

Spiced Fruit Compote ③ POINTS VALUE

level	technique	prep	cook	serves
Basic	Simmer pg. 22	20 min	10 min	8

- ◆ 2 navel oranges
- 2 cups apple cider or unsweetened apple juice
- 3 tablespoons packed brown sugar
- 1 (3-inch) cinnamon stick
- 1 (7-ounce) bag mixed dried fruit (such as apples, pears, apricots, and dried plums)
- ½ cup tart dried cherries
- ½ teaspoon vanilla extract

1 With vegetable peeler, remove 4 strips of orange peel, each about 1 inch wide and 3 inches long. Reserve oranges. Combine orange peel, apple cider, brown sugar, and cinnamon stick in medium saucepan. Set over medium-high heat and bring to boil, stirring until sugar is dissolved. Reduce heat and simmer 5 minutes.

2 Add mixed dried fruit and cherries and simmer, covered, until fruit softens, about 5 minutes. Stir in vanilla extract. Pour fruit mixture into bowl and let cool to room temperature.

3 Remove and discard cinnamon stick. Section oranges (see box, at right). Gently stir orange sections into fruit mixture. Cover and refrigerate overnight.

PER SERVING (½ cup fruit with juices): 159 Cal, 0 g Fat, 0 g Sat Fat, 0 g Trans Fat, 0 mg Chol, 8 mg Sod, 40 g Carb, 3 g Fib, 1 g Prot, 40 mg Calc.

◆ FILLING EXTRA

Serve this compote topped with yogurt for a healthful breakfast (½ cup plain fat-free yogurt will increase the per-serving **POINTS** value by *1*).

HOW TO...
Section Citrus

With a sharp, thin-bladed knife, cut one slice from the top and one slice from the bottom of the fruit. Stand the fruit upright on a cutting board. Following the curve of the fruit, cut away the peel and white pith from top to bottom, turning the fruit as you cut.

Holding the fruit over a bowl to catch the juices, cut between the membranes to the center to release the sections.

Fresh Apple Coffeecake with Pecan Streusel (4 POINTS VALUE)

level	technique	prep	cook	serves
Basic	Bake pg. 27	20 min	30 min	12

STREUSEL
- 1/3 cup pecans, chopped
- 3 tablespoons white whole wheat flour
- 3 tablespoons packed light brown sugar
- 1 tablespoon canola oil
- 3/4 teaspoon cinnamon

CAKE
- 2 cups white whole wheat flour
- 1/2 cup granulated sugar
- 2 teaspoons baking powder
- 1/2 teaspoon baking soda
- 1/2 teaspoon cinnamon
- 1/4 teaspoon salt
- ♦ 1 (6-ounce) container plain fat-free yogurt
- ♦ 1/2 cup unsweetened applesauce
- 2 tablespoons butter, melted
- 2 tablespoons canola oil
- ♦ 1 large egg
- ♦ 1 Granny Smith apple, peeled, cored, and diced

1 Preheat oven to 375°F. Spray 9-inch square baking pan with nonstick spray.

2 To make streusel, stir together pecans, flour, brown sugar, oil, and cinnamon in small bowl until blended.

3 To make cake, stir together flour, granulated sugar, baking powder, baking soda, cinnamon, and salt in large bowl. Whisk together yogurt, applesauce, butter, oil, and egg in medium bowl. Add yogurt mixture and apple to flour mixture; stir just until flour is moistened.

4 Spoon batter into pan and spread evenly. Sprinkle with streusel. Bake until toothpick inserted in center comes out clean, about 30 minutes. Let cool in pan on wire rack. To serve, cut into 12 pieces.

PER SERVING (1/12 of coffeecake): 215 Cal, 8 g Fat, 2 g Sat Fat, 0 g Trans Fat, 23 mg Chol, 215 mg Sod, 33 g Carb, 3 g Fib, 5 g Prot, 92 mg Calc.

Buttermilk-Maple Bran Muffins

level	technique	prep	cook	serves
Basic	Bake pg. 27	15 min	20 min	12

1½ cups shredded bran cereal
½ cup currants
½ cup boiling water
¼ cup canola oil
1 cup low-fat buttermilk
¼ cup pure maple syrup
♦ 1 large egg
1⅓ cups whole wheat pastry flour
1¼ teaspoons baking soda
¼ teaspoon salt
½ cup pecans, chopped

1 Stir together cereal, currants, water, and oil in a large bowl until moistened; let cool slightly.

2 Add buttermilk, maple syrup, and egg; stir until mixed well. Whisk together flour, baking soda, and salt in small bowl. Add flour mixture and pecans to cereal mixture and stir just until flour mixture is moistened. Cover bowl with plastic wrap; let stand 15 minutes.

3 Meanwhile, preheat oven to 400°F. Line 12-cup muffin pan with paper liners.

4 Fill muffin cups evenly with batter. Bake until toothpick inserted into centers comes out clean, 20–25 minutes. Let cool in pan on wire rack 10 minutes. Remove muffins from pan and let cool completely on rack.

PER SERVING (1 muffin): 185 Cal, 9 g Fat, 1 g Sat Fat, 0 g Trans Fat, 18 mg Chol, 228 mg Sod, 26 g Carb, 5 g Fib, 5 g Prot, 73 mg Calc.

BUTTERMILK-MAPLE BRAN MUFFINS
AND LEMON CORN MUFFINS WITH
RASPBERRIES, PAGE 78

Lemon Corn Muffins with Raspberries

3 POINTS VALUE

level	technique	prep	cook	serves
Basic	Bake pg. 27	10 min	15 min	12

1½ cups all-purpose flour
½ cup cornmeal
6 tablespoons sugar
1½ teaspoons baking powder
½ teaspoon baking soda
¼ teaspoon salt
1 cup low-fat buttermilk
3 tablespoons canola oil
♦ 1 large egg
1 tablespoon grated lemon zest (about 2 lemons)
♦ 1½ cups fresh or frozen raspberries

1 Preheat oven to 400°F. Line 12-cup muffin pan with paper liners.

2 Whisk together flour, cornmeal, 5 tablespoons sugar, baking powder, baking soda, and salt in large bowl. Whisk together buttermilk, oil, egg, and lemon zest in small bowl. Add buttermilk mixture to flour mixture and stir just until flour mixture is moistened. Gently stir in raspberries.

3 Fill muffin cups evenly with batter and sprinkle evenly with remaining 1 tablespoon sugar. Bake until muffins spring back when lightly pressed, 15–20 minutes. Let cool in pan on wire rack 5 minutes. Remove muffins from pan and let cool on rack about 15 minutes longer. Serve warm.

PER SERVING (1 muffin): 159 Cal, 4 g Fat, 1 g Sat Fat, 0 g Trans Fat, 18 mg Chol, 190 mg Sod, 27 g Carb, 2 g Fib, 3 g Prot, 67 mg Calc.

HOW TO...
Freeze Raspberries

Discard stems, leaves, and blemished berries. Do not wash. Spread berries out in a single layer on a jelly-roll pan lined with wax paper. Freeze until hard, 1–2 hours.

Transfer berries to heavy-duty zip-close plastic bags. Squeeze out air and seal. When ready to use, rinse berries in a colander under cold running water.

Orange-Glazed Cranberry Scones (2) POINTS VALUE

level	technique	prep	cook	serves
Intermediate	Bake pg. 27	15 min	10 min	24

2 cups all-purpose flour
¼ cup granulated sugar
1 teaspoon baking powder
¼ teaspoon baking soda
¼ teaspoon salt
3 tablespoons cold unsalted butter, cut into pieces
½ cup dried cranberries
¾ cup low-fat buttermilk
♦ 1 large egg
1 tablespoon grated orange zest
1 cup confectioners' sugar
4 teaspoons fresh orange juice

1 Preheat oven to 400°F. Spray large baking sheet with nonstick spray.

2 Whisk together flour, granulated sugar, baking powder, baking soda, and salt in large bowl. With pastry blender or 2 knives used scissor-fashion, cut in butter until mixture resembles fine crumbs with some small pieces of butter remaining. Stir in cranberries. Whisk together buttermilk, egg, and orange zest in small bowl. Add to flour mixture and stir just until dough forms.

3 Gather dough into ball and place on lightly floured surface; lightly knead 2 times. With floured rolling pin, roll dough to ¾-inch thickness. With 1½-inch round cookie cutter, cut out rounds, dipping cutter into flour between cuts to prevent sticking. Place scones on baking sheet about 1 inch apart. Gently gather scraps; reroll and cut out more scones. Bake until golden brown, 10–12 minutes. Let cool on baking sheet on rack until warm, about 10 minutes.

4 Stir together confectioners' sugar and orange juice in small bowl until smooth. Place sheet of wax paper under rack. Dip tops of scones in glaze; place, glaze side up, on rack. Let stand until glaze sets, about 1 hour.

PER SERVING (1 scone): 92 Cal, 2 g Fat, 1 g Sat Fat, 0 g Trans Fat, 13 mg Chol, 66 mg Sod, 17 g Carb, 0 g Fib, 2 g Prot, 20 mg Calc.

CHAPTER 4

20-Minute Main Dishes

Quicker—and far healthier—than the drive-thru, these almost-instant meals will have you and your family enjoying great food fast. With almost three weeks of 20-minute dinner options, you'll never be bored. Make these your go-to recipes when life gets too busy for you to spend time in the kitchen.

Beef Tenderloin and Arugula with Balsamic Sauce ⑤ POINTS VALUE

level	technique	prep	cook	serves
Basic	Pan Sear pg. 20	10 min	10 min	4

- 3/4 cup balsamic vinegar
- 1 tablespoon packed brown sugar
- 1 teaspoon extra-virgin olive oil
- ♦ 4 (1/4-pound) filet mignons, 1/2 inch thick, trimmed
- 1/2 teaspoon salt
- 1/4 teaspoon coarsely ground black pepper
- ♦ 6 cups lightly packed baby arugula

1 Combine vinegar and brown sugar in small saucepan; bring to boil over medium-high heat. Boil until mixture is reduced to syrupy glaze, about 8 minutes. Remove saucepan from heat; whisk in oil.

2 Meanwhile, spray large nonstick skillet with nonstick spray and set over medium-high heat. Sprinkle filets mignons with salt and pepper. Add steaks to skillet and cook until instant-read thermometer inserted into side of each steak registers 145°F for medium, about 4 minutes on each side.

3 Divide arugula evenly among 4 plates and top each portion with a steak. Drizzle with the balsamic glaze and serve at once.

PER SERVING (1½ cups arugula, 1 steak, and 1 tablespoon glaze): 222 Cal, 9 g Fat, 3 g Sat Fat, 0 g Trans Fat, 49 mg Chol, 341 mg Sod, 5 g Carb, 1 g Fib, 27 g Prot, 62 mg Calc.

◆ FILLING EXTRA

Serve the steak with a side of potatoes. Place 2 medium potatoes cut into wedges, in a microwavable dish; cover with wax paper. Microwave on High until the potatoes are tender, 5–6 minutes. Sprinkle with salt and pepper. The per-serving **POINTS** value will increase by **1.**

BEEF TENDERLOIN AND ARUGULA WITH BALSAMIC SAUCE

Broiled Flank Steak with
Fennel-Coriander Rub (4 POINTS VALUE)

level	technique	prep	cook	serves
Basic	Broil pg. 25	10 min	10 min	4

1	tablespoon black peppercorns
1	tablespoon fennel seeds
1	tablespoon coriander seeds
1	tablespoon packed brown sugar
2	teaspoons paprika
2	garlic cloves
♦ 1	(1-pound) flank steak, trimmed
¼	teaspoon salt

1 Combine peppercorns, fennel seeds, coriander seeds, brown sugar, paprika, and garlic in spice grinder or mini–food processor; pulse until coarsely ground. Press spice mixture on both sides of steak. Place steak in a zip-close plastic bag. Squeeze out air and seal bag. Refrigerate, 1 hour or up to overnight.

2 Spray broiler rack with nonstick spray and preheat broiler.

3 Sprinkle steak with salt and place on broiler rack. Broil steak 5 inches from heat until instant-read thermometer inserted into center of steak registers 145°F for medium-rare, about 5 minutes on each side. Transfer steak to a cutting board and let stand about 5 minutes. Cut steak on an angle against the grain into 12 slices.

PER SERVING (3 slices steak): 208 Cal, 8 g Fat, 3 g Sat Fat, 0 g Trans Fat, 49 mg Chol, 186 mg Sod, 6 g Carb, 2 g Fib, 27 g Prot, 45 mg Calc.

HOW TO...
Toast Spices

Toasting whole spices such as fennel seeds, coriander seeds, and whole peppercorns brings out their flavors and gives them a smoky taste.

To do so, put them into a small heavy skillet and place over medium heat. Toast, stirring the spices often, until fragrant, about 3 minutes.

Lemongrass Burgers (6 POINTS VALUE)

level	technique	prep	cook	serves
Basic	Pan Sear pg. 20	10 min	10 min	4

- ♦ 1   pound ground lean beef (7% fat or less)
-    2   tablespoons reduced-sodium soy sauce
-    1   tablespoon minced lemongrass
-    1   shallot, minced
-    1   teaspoon Asian (dark) sesame oil
-    1   garlic clove, minced
-    4   multigrain hamburger buns, toasted
- ♦ 4   thin slices red onion
- ♦ 4   red bell pepper rings
- ♦ 8   lettuce leaves

1 Combine beef, soy sauce, lemongrass, shallot, oil, and garlic in medium bowl. With damp hands, form mixture into 4 ($\frac{1}{2}$-inch-thick) patties.

2 Spray medium nonstick skillet with nonstick spray and set over medium-high heat. Add patties and cook until instant-read thermometer inserted into side of each patty registers 160°F for medium, 5–6 minutes on each side.

3 Place burgers in buns with onion, pepper rings, and lettuce leaves.

PER SERVING (1 burger): 285 Cal, 8 g Fat, 3 g Sat Fat, 0 g Trans Fat, 60 mg Chol, 462 mg Sod, 24 g Carb, 2 g Fib, 28 g Prot, 78 mg Calc.

IN THE KITCHEN

Lemongrass looks like a sturdy scallion. To use it, cut away and discard the green top and remove the toughest outer layers from the white bottom. Mince the innermost layers to release its citrusy flavor. If lemongrass is not available, substitute $1\frac{1}{2}$ teaspoons each of grated lemon and lime zest in this recipe.

EASY MOO SHU PORK

Easy Moo Shu Pork (4 POINTS VALUE)

level	technique	prep	cook	serves
Basic	Stir-Fry pg. 19	10 min	10 min	4

- 4   tablespoons reduced-sodium soy sauce
- 1   tablespoon cornstarch
- ♦ ½   pound pork tenderloin, cut into thin 1-inch strips
- ♦ 3   large egg whites, lightly beaten
- 2   garlic cloves, minced
- 1   tablespoon minced peeled fresh ginger
- ♦ 5   cups shredded Napa cabbage
- ♦ 1   cup sliced white mushrooms
- ♦ 5   scallions, sliced
- 1   teaspoon Asian (dark) sesame oil
- 4   whole wheat tortillas, warmed

1 Whisk 2 tablespoons of soy sauce and cornstarch in small bowl until blended; add pork and toss to coat.

2 Spray large deep nonstick skillet or wok with nonstick spray and set over medium heat until a drop of water sizzles on it. Add egg whites and stir-fry until firm, about 2 minutes. Transfer to plate.

3 Spray same pan with nonstick spray and increase heat to medium-high. Add pork; stir-fry until no longer pink, about 2 minutes. Add garlic and ginger; stir-fry 1 minute. Add cabbage, mushrooms, and scallions; stir-fry until cabbage starts to wilt, about 3 minutes. Add egg, remaining 2 tablespoons soy sauce, and oil and stir-fry until heated through, about 1 minute.

4 Spoon about 1 cup of pork mixture onto each tortilla and roll up to enclose filling.

PER SERVING (1 filled tortilla): 219 Cal, 5 g Fat, 1 g Sat Fat, 0 g Trans Fat, 24 mg Chol, 849 mg Sod, 26 g Carb, 5 g Fib, 20 g Prot, 125 mg Calc.

Green Peppercorn Pork Chops (5 POINTS VALUE)

level	technique	prep	cook	serves
Basic	Pan Sear pg. 20, Roast pg. 24	10 min	10 min	4

- 2 tablespoons dried whole green peppercorns, crushed
- ♦ 4 (¼-pound) boneless center-cut pork loin chops, about ½ inch thick, trimmed
- ¼ teaspoon salt
- 2 teaspoons olive oil
- ½ cup dry red wine
- ♦ ¾ cup Chicken Stock (page 32) or store-bought reduced-sodium chicken broth
- 1½ teaspoons coarse-grained Dijon mustard
- ♦ ½ teaspoon tomato paste

1 Preheat oven to 400°F.

2 Press peppercorns on both sides of pork chops; sprinkle with salt.

3 Heat oil in large nonstick skillet over medium-high heat. Add chops and cook until browned, about 2 minutes on each side. Transfer chops to small baking sheet and roast until cooked through, about 6 minutes.

4 Meanwhile, add wine to skillet; cook over high heat, scraping up all browned bits on bottom of skillet. Boil until wine is reduced to ¼ cup, about 1 minute. Add stock and return to boil; cook about 2 minutes. Whisk in mustard and tomato paste until blended; cook until sauce is thickened and reduced to about ½ cup, about 1 minute longer. Transfer chops to 4 plates and top evenly with sauce.

PER SERVING (1 chop and 2 tablespoons sauce): 227 Cal, 11 g Fat, 4 g Sat Fat, 0 g Trans Fat, 71 mg Chol, 314 mg Sod, 3 g Carb, 1 g Fib, 26 g Prot, 21 mg Calc.

◆ FILLING EXTRA

Serve steamed kale with the pork chops. Trim and thinly slice 1 pound of kale and steam until tender, about 8 minutes. Sprinkle with salt and black pepper to taste.

Creamy Chicken Paprikash (7 POINTS VALUE)

level	technique	prep	cook	serves
Basic	Sauté pg. 18, Simmer pg. 22	5 min	15 min	4

3	cups wide yolk-free whole wheat noodles
♦ 4	(5-ounce) skinless boneless chicken breasts
3	teaspoons smoked sweet paprika
½	teaspoon salt
¼	teaspoon cayenne
1	teaspoon canola oil
♦ 1	large onion, diced
⅛	teaspoon ground cloves
♦ ¾	cup Chicken Stock (page 32) or store-bought reduced-sodium chicken broth
½	cup reduced-fat sour cream
1½	teaspoons all-purpose flour
2	tablespoons chopped fresh parsley

1 Cook noodles according to package directions, omitting salt if desired; drain.

2 Meanwhile, sprinkle chicken with 2 teaspoons of paprika, salt, and cayenne. Heat oil in large nonstick skillet over medium-high heat. Add chicken and cook, turning once, until well browned, 3 minutes. Transfer to plate.

3 Add onion, cloves, and remaining 1 teaspoon paprika to skillet; cook, stirring frequently, until onion is lightly browned, about 4 minutes. Add stock and cook, scraping up browned bits from bottom of pan. Whisk in sour cream and flour until blended; bring to boil. Return chicken to skillet and reduce heat to low. Cover and simmer until chicken is cooked through, about 4 minutes. With tongs, transfer chicken to plate.

4 Stir noodles into sauce in skillet and cook until heated through, about 2 minutes. Divide noodles and sauce among 4 plates and top with chicken. Sprinkle evenly with parsley.

PER SERVING (1 chicken breast with ¾ cup noodles and sauce): 345 Cal, 10 g Fat, 4 g Sat Fat, 0 g Trans Fat, 100 mg Chol, 565 mg Sod, 29 g Carb, 4 g Fib, 39 g Prot, 76 mg Calc.

8 Kitchen Shortcuts

Try these timesavers to get you out of the kitchen fast.

Chop Right Chop onions, celery, or carrots for soups, casseroles, or meatloaf in a food processor.

Sharpen Up Sharp knives and peelers get the job done faster. If your vegetable peeler is dull, replace it with a new one.

Bag It Buy frozen veggies in bags rather than boxes. The pieces aren't stuck together so they thaw faster and you can easily take what you need for a recipe from the bag.

Think Small Foods cut into small pieces cook faster. Slice poultry, meats, and vegetables into thin slices or small cubes before cooking.

Buy Some Time Pre-prepped ingredients cost a little more, but are worth it when you are in a time crunch. Pre-washed salad greens, cut-up vegetables, minced garlic, shredded cheese, peeled shrimp, and rotisserie chicken will help you get dinner done faster.

Turn Up the Heat To bring water to a boil quickly, start with hot tap water, set the burner on the highest heat setting, and cover the pot with a lid.

Keep On Cooking Make the most of time spent waiting for water to boil or the oven to preheat by chopping ingredients for the main dish or making a salad to serve alongside.

Clean as You Go As you use bowls, measuring cups, and pans, wash or stack them in the dishwasher when you have a minute. This clears up counter space and saves time with final clean up.

Indian-Spiced Chicken with Mango Raita ⑤

level	technique	prep	cook	serves
Basic	Sauté pg. 18	10 min	10 min	4

- ½ cup fat-free plain Greek yogurt
- 1 tablespoon honey
- 1 teaspoon grated peeled fresh ginger
- 1 teaspoon garam masala
- ½ teaspoon salt
- ¼ teaspoon black pepper
- 4 (5-ounce) skinless boneless chicken breasts
- 1 small ripe mango, peeled, pitted, and diced
- 1 Kirby cucumber, diced
- 2 tablespoons thinly sliced fresh mint

1 Whisk together ¼ cup yogurt, 1½ teaspoons honey, ginger, garam masala, salt, and pepper in medium bowl. Add chicken, turning to coat evenly.

2 To make raita, whisk together remaining ¼ cup yogurt and 1½ teaspoons honey in serving bowl until blended. Stir in mango, cucumber, and mint.

3 Spray large nonstick skillet with nonstick spray and set over medium-high heat. Add chicken and cook, turning occasionally, until cooked through, about 8 minutes. Serve with raita.

PER SERVING (1 chicken breast and about ⅓ cup raita): 253 Cal, 5 g Fat, 1 g Sat Fat, 0 g Trans Fat, 89 mg Chol, 401 mg Sod, 16 g Carb, 1 g Fib, 34 g Prot, 94 mg Calc.

IN THE KITCHEN

A raita is a cooling condiment served to counterbalance spicy Indian dishes. Raitas always contain yogurt and are flavored using a variety of fruits, vegetables, herbs, and spices.

**INDIAN-SPICED CHICKEN
WITH MANGO RAITA**

Mahogany Chicken Thighs (7 POINTS VALUE)

level	technique	prep	cook	serves
Basic	Simmer pg. 22	10 min	10 min	4

⅓ cup water

3 tablespoons reduced-sodium soy sauce

2 tablespoons mirin or dry sherry

1½ teaspoons grated peeled fresh ginger

1 garlic clove, minced

2 teaspoons sugar

1 teaspoon cornstarch

♦ 4 (¼-pound) skinless boneless chicken thighs, trimmed

½ teaspoon black pepper

♦ 2 cups hot cooked brown rice

1 Whisk together water, soy sauce, mirin, ginger, garlic, sugar, and cornstarch in small bowl.

2 Sprinkle chicken thighs with pepper. Spray large nonstick skillet with nonstick spray and set over medium-high heat. Add chicken and cook until browned, about 2 minutes on each side. Re-whisk cornstarch mixture. Add to skillet and bring to boil. Reduce heat to medium-low and simmer, spooning sauce over chicken, until cooked through and glazed, about 6 minutes. Serve with rice.

PER SERVING (1 chicken thigh, about 1 tablespoon sauce, and ½ cup rice): 315 Cal, 10 g Fat, 3 g Sat Fat, 0 g Trans Fat, 70 mg Chol, 467 mg Sod, 28 g Carb, 3 g Fib, 27 g Prot, 41 mg Calc.

♦ FILLING EXTRA

Serve the chicken with steamed bok choy. Cut 8 baby bok choy in half lengthwise and steam until crisp-tender, about 3 minutes. Drizzle with reduced-sodium soy sauce.

Chicken with Moroccan Spices

level	technique	prep	cook	serves
Basic	Sauté pg. 18	10 min	10 min	4

- 2 teaspoons grated lemon zest
- 1 teaspoon olive oil
- 1 teaspoon grated peeled fresh ginger
- 1 teaspoon ground coriander
- 3/4 teaspoon cinnamon
- 3/4 teaspoon ground cumin
- ♦ 4 (1/4-pound) skinless boneless chicken thighs, trimmed
- 1/2 teaspoon salt
- 1 tablespoon chopped fresh flat-leaf parsley
- 4 lemon wedges

1 Combine lemon zest, oil, ginger, coriander, cinnamon, and cumin in large zip-close plastic bag and add chicken. Squeeze out air and seal bag; turn to coat chicken. Refrigerate at least 1 hour or up to 4 hours.

2 Spray large nonstick skillet with nonstick spray and set over medium-high heat. Sprinkle chicken with salt. Add chicken to skillet and cook, turning occasionally, until well browned and cooked through, about 8 minutes. Sprinkle chicken with parsley and serve with lemon wedges.

PER SERVING (1 chicken thigh): 200 Cal, 10 g Fat, 3 g Sat Fat, 0 g Trans Fat, 70 mg Chol, 359 mg Sod, 2 g Carb, 1 g Fib, 24 g Prot, 43 mg Calc.

◆ FILLING EXTRA

Serve the chicken with a quick side dish of whole wheat couscous (1/2 cup cooked whole wheat couscous per serving will increase the **POINTS** value by **2**). This recipe works with the Simply Filling technique.

Thai Chicken Fried Rice with Scallions and Mint ⑥ POINTS VALUE

level	technique	prep	cook	serves
Basic	Stir-Fry pg. 19	10 min	10 min	4

- ♦ 1 tablespoon tomato paste
- 1 tablespoon Asian fish sauce
- 3 teaspoons canola oil
- ♦ 2 large eggs, lightly beaten
- ♦ 3 scallions, thinly sliced
- 2 garlic cloves, minced
- ♦ 2 cups cooked brown rice
- ♦ 1½ cups diced cooked chicken breast
- ♦ 2 plum tomatoes, cut into wedges
- 1 tablespoon chopped fresh mint

1 Whisk together tomato paste and fish sauce in small bowl until smooth.

2 Heat large nonstick skillet or wok over medium-high heat until a drop of water sizzles on it. Pour in 1 teaspoon oil and swirl to coat pan; add eggs. Stir-fry until firm, about 2 minutes. Transfer eggs to plate.

3 Heat remaining 2 teaspoons oil in same pan. Add scallions and garlic; stir-fry until softened, about 3 minutes. Add rice and chicken; stir-fry until rice is coated, about 1 minute. Add tomatoes and tomato paste mixture; stir-fry until the tomatoes are softened, about 2 minutes. Remove pan from heat; stir in eggs and mint.

PER SERVING (1 cup): 281 Cal, 9 g Fat, 2 g Sat Fat, 0 g Trans Fat, 149 mg Chol, 542 mg Sod, 26 g Carb, 4 g Fib, 22 g Prot, 48 mg Calc.

♦ FILLING EXTRA

Add 1 thinly sliced zucchini along with the scallions in step 3. This recipe works with the Simply Filling technique.

Turkey Soup with Sweet Potato and Dill ④ POINTS VALUE

level	technique	prep	cook	serves
Basic	Simmer pg. 22	10 min	15 min	6

- ♦ 1 pound turkey breast cutlets, cut into 1-inch strips
- ♦ 6 cups Chicken Stock (page 32) or store-bought reduced-sodium chicken broth
- 3 cups wide yolk-free whole wheat noodles
- ♦ 1 large sweet potato, peeled and cut into ½-inch pieces
- ♦ 1 large onion, diced
- ♦ 1 jalapeño pepper, seeded and minced
- ♦ 2 yellow squash, quartered lengthwise and cut into 1-inch chunks
- ½ cup chopped fresh dill
- 1 teaspoon reduced-sodium soy sauce
- 1 lime, cut into 6 wedges

1 Spray nonstick Dutch oven with canola nonstick spray and set over medium-high heat. Add turkey and cook, stirring frequently, until well browned, about 3 minutes. Transfer to plate.

2 Add stock and bring to boil. Add noodles, potato, onion, and jalapeño. Reduce heat and simmer, covered, until potato is almost tender, about 7 minutes. Add squash, dill, and soy sauce; cook until noodles and vegetables are just tender, about 3 minutes longer. Serve with lime wedges.

PER SERVING (about 2 cups): 237 Cal, 3 g Fat, 1 g Sat Fat, 0 g Trans Fat, 51 mg Chol, 442 mg Sod, 29 g Carb, 4 g Fib, 27 g Prot, 56 mg Calc.

IN THE KITCHEN

You can substitute cut-up chicken tenders or thin strips of pork tenderloin for the turkey if you like. Diced butternut squash can be used instead of the sweet potato. This recipe works with the Simply Filling technique.

4 Fast Ideas

The key to getting dinner on the table in no time involves a little pre-planning at all stages of the meal prep.

Shop Smart Sort groceries before you get home. At the market, ask the bagger to separate the perishables from the pantry items. Once you're home, the unpacking will go quickly and you'll be able to get the cooking started faster.

Jump-Start Steal this time-saving trick employed by TV chefs: Before you begin preparing a meal, gather all your ingredients and tools and arrange them on your counter in roughly the order in which you'll need them.

Spice Check Measure all the spices you'll need in advance and mix them in a small bowl. Not only will you get a head start on prep, but you'll also be less likely to forget ingredients.

Speed up Measuring Buy a few extra sets of measuring spoons, take them apart, and store them individually. Then you won't waste time washing or holding on to extra spoons when you only need one.

Tuna with Cilantro-Ginger Sauce

level	technique	prep	cook	serves
Basic	Pan Sear pg. 20	5 min	10 min	4

⅓	cup chopped fresh cilantro
◆ 3	tablespoons finely chopped scallions
1	tablespoon minced peeled fresh ginger
1	garlic clove, minced
3	tablespoons orange juice
1	tablespoon lemon juice
2	teaspoons extra-virgin olive oil
¾	teaspoon salt
◆ 4	(5-ounce) tuna steaks

1 To make sauce, stir together cilantro, scallions, ginger, garlic, orange juice, lemon juice, oil, and ¼ teaspoon salt in small bowl.

2 Sprinkle tuna with remaining ½ teaspoon salt. Spray large nonstick skillet with nonstick spray and set over medium-high heat. Add tuna and cook 2–3 minutes on each side for medium-rare or until desired doneness. Serve tuna with sauce.

PER SERVING (1 tuna steak and 2 tablespoons sauce): 189 Cal, 4 g Fat, 1 g Sat Fat, 0 g Trans Fat, 66 mg Chol, 491 mg Sod, 2 g Carb, 0 g Fib, 34 g Prot, 32 mg Calc.

IN THE KITCHEN

You can substitute chopped fresh basil for the cilantro in this recipe. The sauce is a perfect complement to any simply prepared fish, shrimp, or scallops.

Shrimp Fra Diavolo (5 POINTS VALUE)

level	technique	prep	cook	serves
Basic	Sauté pg. 18, Simmer pg. 22	5 min	15 min	4

♦ 6   ounces whole wheat capellini

1   tablespoon olive oil

1   shallot, chopped

2   garlic cloves, minced

♦ $3/4$ pound peeled and deveined medium shrimp

♦ 1   cup Homemade Marinara Sauce (page 34) or store-bought tomato sauce

♦ 1   cup frozen green peas

$1/4$ teaspoon red pepper flakes

2   tablespoons chopped fresh parsley

1 Cook capellini according to package directions, omitting salt if desired. Drain, reserving $1/4$ cup cooking water.

2 Meanwhile, heat oil in large nonstick skillet over medium-high heat. Add shallot and garlic; cook, stirring, 1 minute. Add shrimp and cook, stirring often, until almost opaque in center, about 1 minute.

3 Add marinara sauce, peas, and pepper flakes to skillet; bring to boil. Reduce heat and simmer until shrimp are just opaque in center, about 2 minutes. Stir in reserved cooking water. Transfer capellini to serving platter and top with shrimp and sauce. Sprinkle with parsley.

PER SERVING ($3/4$ cup shrimp and sauce with $3/4$ cup pasta): 292 Cal, 5 g Fat, 1 g Sat Fat, 0 g Trans Fat, 121 mg Chol, 532 mg Sod, 41 g Carb, 6 g Fib, 22 g Prot, 84 mg Calc.

IN THE KITCHEN

Fra Diavolo is Italian for "brother devil" and is used to describe a spicy dish. Reduce the pepper flakes to $1/8$ teaspoon if you prefer a dish with less heat. This recipe works with the Simply Filling technique.

MISO-CRUSTED COD

Miso-Crusted Cod (4 POINTS VALUE)

level	technique	prep	cook	serves
Basic	Roast pg. 24	5 min	10 min	4

  2   tablespoons white miso
  2   tablespoons packed brown sugar
♦ 4   (5-ounce) cod fillets, about 1 inch thick
♦ 2   tablespoons thinly sliced scallions

1 Preheat oven to 425°F and spray a shallow roasting pan with nonstick spray.

2 Stir together miso and brown sugar in small bowl; spread over both sides of cod.

3 Place cod in roasting pan; sprinkle with scallions. Roast fish until just opaque in center, about 10 minutes.

PER SERVING (1 cod fillet): 145 Cal, 1 g Fat, 0 g Sat Fat, 0 g Trans Fat, 54 mg Chol, 314 mg Sod, 10 g Carb, 0 g Fib, 23 g Prot, 20 mg Calc.

IN THE KITCHEN

Miso is fermented soybean paste. You'll find it in the refrigerated section of Asian markets, natural-foods stores, and large supermarkets. It is a staple in Japanese cooking and adds a salty, mellow flavor to dishes.

Lentils and Rice with Caramelized Onions (4 POINTS VALUE)

level	technique	prep	cook	serves
Basic	Simmer pg. 22	5 min	15 min	4

- ◆ 3/4 cup green (French) lentils, picked over and rinsed
- ◆ 3 cups Vegetable Stock (page 30) or store-bought reduced-sodium vegetable broth
-   1 1/4 teaspoons ground cumin
- ◆ 1 cup quick-cooking brown rice
- ◆ 1 extra-large sweet onion, halved and thinly sliced
- ◆ 1/2 cup fat-free plain yogurt

1 Combine lentils, stock, and cumin in medium saucepan; bring to boil over high heat. Reduce heat and simmer, covered, 5 minutes. Stir in rice and simmer, covered, until lentils are just tender and still hold their shape and rice has absorbed all cooking liquid, about 10 minutes. Remove saucepan from heat and let stand 3 minutes.

2 Meanwhile, spray large nonstick skillet with nonstick spray and set over medium heat. Add onion and cook, stirring frequently, until deep golden, about 15 minutes.

3 Spoon lentils evenly on 4 plates and top evenly with onion and yogurt.

PER SERVING (3/4 cup lentils and rice, 1/4 cup onion, and 2 tablespoons yogurt): 250 Cal, 1 g Fat, 0 g Sat Fat, 0 g Trans Fat, 1 mg Chol, 346 mg Sod, 47 g Carb, 9 g Fib, 13 g Prot, 107 mg Calc.

IN THE KITCHEN

The key to success when caramelizing onions is to cook them over medium heat, so their natural sugars slowly turn golden brown. If the onions are cooked over a higher heat, they may burn before they caramelize. This recipe works with the Simply Filling technique.

Gnocchi with Swiss Chard and Red Pepper Sauce

6 POINTS VALUE

level	technique	prep	cook	serves
Basic	Boil, Simmer pg. 22	5 min	15 min	4

- 1 (17½-ounce) package refrigerated whole wheat gnocchi
- ♦ 1 (12-ounce) jar roasted red peppers (not in oil), rinsed and drained or 1½ cups roasted red peppers (see box at right)
- ♦ ½ (14-ounce) package light silken tofu
- 1 tablespoon olive oil
- 2 garlic cloves, minced
- ♦ 1 pound Swiss chard, tough stems removed, leaves thinly sliced and rinsed
- ¼ teaspoon black pepper
- 2 tablespoons shaved pecorino or Parmesan cheese

1 Cook gnocchi according to package directions, omitting salt if desired; drain and keep warm.

2 Meanwhile, combine roasted peppers and tofu in blender; process until mixture is smooth.

3 Heat oil in large skillet over medium heat. Add garlic and cook, stirring constantly, 1 minute. Add Swiss chard and water that clings to its leaves; cook, covered, until wilted, about 3 minutes. Uncover and cook until tender, about 5 minutes longer. Add roasted pepper mixture to skillet; reduce heat to low and simmer about 2 minutes. Add gnocchi and cook, stirring, until heated through and coated with sauce. Sprinkle with pecorino.

PER SERVING (about 1½ cups): 299 Cal, 5 g Fat, 1 g Sat Fat, 0 g Trans Fat, 2 mg Chol, 905 mg Sod, 54 g Carb, 4 g Fib, 11 g Prot, 122 mg Calc.

IN THE KITCHEN

Freshly roasted and peeled red and yellow bell peppers are available in the prepared food sections of some supermarkets. These peppers tend to be a bit sweeter than some brands of bottled peppers.

HOW TO...
Roast Bell Peppers

1

Preheat the broiler and line a baking pan with foil. Cut each bell pepper in half lengthwise and remove the stems and seeds. Place, cut side down, on the pan and broil 5 inches from the heat, until well charred, about 10 minutes.

2

Transfer the peppers to a bowl and cover. Let the peppers steam for 10 minutes. When cool enough to handle, peel away the skin and discard. Peppers may also be steamed inside a closed paper bag.

SPINACH, ARTICHOKE, AND OLIVE PIZZA

Spinach, Artichoke, and Olive Pizza

level	technique	prep	cook	serves
Basic	Bake pg. 27	5 min	10 min	6

- ♦ 1 (8-ounce) microwavable bag baby spinach leaves
- 1 (10-ounce) prebaked thin whole wheat pizza crust
- ½ cup marinated artichoke hearts, rinsed, drained, and chopped
- ♦ 6 Kalamata olives, pitted and sliced
- ½ cup shredded Gruyère cheese
- ½ cup shredded part-skim mozzarella cheese

1 Preheat oven to 450°F. Spray baking sheet with nonstick spray.

2 Microwave spinach according to package directions.

3 Place crust on baking sheet. Top crust evenly with spinach, artichokes, and olives. Sprinkle evenly with Gruyère and mozzarella. Bake until cheese is melted, about 8 minutes. Cut into 6 wedges.

PER SERVING (1 wedge): 215 Cal, 8 g Fat, 4 g Sat Fat, 0 g Trans Fat, 15 mg Chol, 435 mg Sod, 26 g Carb, 5 g Fib, 12 g Prot, 270 mg Calc.

IN THE KITCHEN

Gruyère is a creamy nutty-flavored cow's milk cheese from Switzerland. You can find it in many supermarkets and gourmet food shops. Or, omit it and double the amount of mozzarella in this recipe if you prefer.

CHAPTER 5

Beef, Pork & Lamb

Succulent meats top almost everyone's list of satisfying foods. Using lean cuts and healthy cooking techniques, you'll produce hearty and nourishing dishes without tipping the scale. Try the familiar flavors of a beef and pasta casserole one day and the exotic taste of burgers with hoisin sauce the next.

Cider-Braised Beef with Root Vegetables (7 POINTS VALUE)

level	technique	prep	cook	serves
Intermediate	Braise pg. 23	15 min	3 hr 15 min	8

- ♦ 1 (2-pound) beef bottom round roast, trimmed
- 1 teaspoon salt
- ¼ teaspoon black pepper
- 2 teaspoons olive oil
- 1½ cups unsweetened apple cider
- 1 cup dry red wine
- 4 garlic cloves, minced
- ♦ 4 medium parsnips, peeled and cut into 1-inch pieces
- ♦ 3 carrots, cut into 1-inch pieces
- ♦ 3 medium red potatoes, scrubbed and each cut into 6 wedges
- ♦ 2 onions, each cut into 6 wedges
- 2 teaspoons dried thyme

1 Preheat oven to 350°F.

2 Sprinkle beef with salt and pepper. Heat oil in Dutch oven over medium-high heat. Add beef and cook, turning occasionally, until browned on all sides, about 8 minutes. Add cider and wine, stirring to scrape any browned bits from bottom of Dutch oven. Add garlic and bring to boil. Cover, transfer pot to oven, and bake 1 hour, turning halfway through.

3 Stir in parsnips, carrots, potatoes, onions, and thyme. Cover and bake until beef and vegetables are fork-tender, about 2 hours. Transfer beef to cutting board and let cool 10 minutes. Cut into 16 slices and serve with vegetables and broth.

PER SERVING (2 slices beef with about ½ cup vegetables and broth): 332 Cal, 14 g Fat, 5 g Sat Fat, 1 g Trans Fat, 69 mg Chol, 394 mg Sod, 29 g Carb, 4 g Fib, 23 g Prot, 47 mg Calc.

◆ FILLING EXTRA

Serve the beef and vegetables with a side of steamed broccoli.

CIDER-BRAISED BEEF WITH ROOT VEGETABLES

Rosemary Roast Beef Tenderloin and Vegetables ⑥ POINTS VALUE

level	technique	prep	cook	serves
Intermediate	Roast pg. 24	15 min	1 hr	8

- 6 large shallots, peeled and halved
- ♦ 2 pounds small red potatoes, halved or quartered if large
- 4 teaspoons extra-virgin olive oil
- 1 teaspoon salt
- 3/4 teaspoon black pepper
- ♦ 1 (2-pound) beef tenderloin, trimmed
- 2 garlic cloves, minced
- 1 tablespoon chopped fresh rosemary
- ♦ 1½ pounds green beans, trimmed

1 Preheat oven to 450°F. Place shallots and potatoes on large rimmed baking sheet. Drizzle with 2 teaspoons of oil, sprinkle with ½ teaspoon salt and ¼ teaspoon pepper and toss to coat. Roast 30 minutes.

2 Meanwhile, rub beef with garlic, ¼ teaspoon remaining salt, and ¼ teaspoon remaining pepper. Spray large skillet with nonstick spray and set over medium-high heat. Place beef in skillet and cook, turning occasionally, until browned on all sides, 10–12 minutes. Rub rosemary over meat.

3 Turn vegetables and push them to sides of baking sheet. Place beef on rack in center of baking sheet and roast until vegetables are browned and tender and instant-read thermometer inserted into center of beef registers 135°F, about 22 minutes. Transfer vegetables to serving platter and cover loosely with foil. Transfer beef to cutting board, cover loosely with foil, and let stand 10 minutes. (The internal temperature will increase to 145°F for medium-rare.)

4 Meanwhile, place green beans on large rimmed baking sheet; drizzle with remaining 2 teaspoons oil, ¼ teaspoon salt, and ¼ teaspoon pepper. Roast, stirring once, until crisp-tender, 10 minutes. Cut beef across grain into 16 slices.

PER SERVING (2 slices beef with 1 cup vegetables): 308 Cal, 10 g Fat, 3 g Sat Fat, 0 g Trans Fat, 46 mg Chol, 342 mg Sod, 30 g Carb, 6 g Fib, 28 g Prot, 68 mg Calc

IN THE KITCHEN

You can substitute fresh thyme for the rosemary in this recipe, or use a mixture of both herbs. This recipe works with the Simply Filling technique.

Grilled Flank Steak with Feta-Herb Sauce

5 POINTS VALUE

level	technique	prep	cook	serves
Basic	Grill pg. 26	15 min	20 min	8

STEAK

- ◆ 1 (2-pound) flank steak, trimmed
- 2 garlic cloves, finely chopped
- 1 teaspoon dried oregano
- ¼ teaspoon salt
- ⅛ teaspoon cayenne

FETA-HERB SAUCE

- ½ cup chopped fresh flat-leaf parsley
- ⅓ cup chopped fresh cilantro
- 2 tablespoons crumbled reduced-fat feta cheese
- 1 tablespoon olive oil
- 1 tablespoon red-wine vinegar
- ◆ 1 jalapeño pepper, seeded and minced

1 Spray grill rack with nonstick spray and preheat grill to medium-high or prepare a medium-high fire.

2 Rub steak with garlic, oregano, salt, and cayenne. Place on grill rack and grill, turning occasionally, until instant-read thermometer inserted into side of steak registers 145°F for medium, 20–25 minutes. Transfer to cutting board and let stand 10 minutes.

3 Meanwhile, to make sauce, stir together all ingredients in a small bowl. Cut steak across the grain into 24 slices. Serve with sauce.

PER SERVING (about 3 slices beef and about 1 tablespoon sauce): 206 Cal, 7 g Fat, 2 g Sat Fat, 0 g Trans Fat, 83 mg Chol, 145 mg Sod, 1 g Carb, 0 g Fib, 34 g Prot, 22 mg Calc.

◆ FILLING EXTRA

Make a grilled vegetable side dish while you grill the steak. Cut 2 bell peppers each into 4 pieces and discard the seeds; spray lightly with nonstick spray. Grill, turning occasionally, until softened, 6–8 minutes. Season to taste with salt and pepper.

HOW TO...
Mince Fresh Herbs

1

Pull the leaves from the stems of the herbs. Gather the leaves into a pile on a cutting board. With a sharp cook's knife, cut across the herbs to chop the leaves coarsely.

2

Carefully steadying the top of the blade with the palm of your hand, rock the knife up and down without lifting the tip from the cutting board until the herbs are minced.

ASIAN BEEF AND
BOK CHOY SALAD

Asian Beef and Bok Choy Salad ⬤ 4 POINTS VALUE

level	technique	prep	cook	serves
Basic	Stir-Fry pg. 19	15 min	5 min	4

♦ 1   pound beef sirloin, trimmed
  2   tablespoons fish sauce
  1   tablespoon reduced-sodium soy sauce
  2   teaspoons grated lime zest
  2   teaspoons sugar
  2   garlic cloves, minced
  ⅓   cup lime juice
      Pinch red pepper flakes
♦ 4   cups thinly sliced bok choy
♦ 4   cups thinly sliced Napa cabbage
  2   shallots, 1 minced and 1 thinly sliced

1 Put beef on plate and place in freezer until very firm, about 30 minutes. Place 1 tablespoon fish sauce, soy sauce, lime zest, 1 teaspoon of sugar, and 1 clove garlic in large zip-close plastic bag. Thinly slice beef and add to bag; turn to coat beef. Refrigerate, turning bag occasionally, 30 minutes.

2 To make dressing, whisk together lime juice and remaining 1 tablespoon fish sauce, 1 teaspoon sugar, and 1 garlic clove in small bowl; stir in pepper flakes. Combine bok choy, cabbage, and shallots in large serving bowl.

3 Spray large deep nonstick skillet or wok with nonstick spray and set over medium-high heat until a drop of water sizzles on it. Add steak and stir-fry until lightly browned, about 1 minute. Add steak and reserved dressing to bok choy mixture; toss to coat.

PER SERVING (2 cups): 208 Cal, 4 g Fat, 1 g Sat Fat, 0 g Trans Fat, 73 mg Chol, 961 mg Sod, 9 g Carb, 2 g Fib, 33 g Prot, 163 mg Calc.

IN THE KITCHEN

You can substitute 4 cups of watercress for the bok choy if you prefer a spicier type of green.

Food Safety

Safe food handling starts at the grocery store and continues as you prepare food at home. At every step you need to minimize risk for contamination and food-borne illnesses. Here are a few guidelines to help keep you and your family safe.

Shop Wise

• Place meats, poultry, and seafood inside plastic bags from the produce department before adding them to your cart. This prevents juices from dripping onto other foods and spreading bacteria.

• Open egg cartons to make sure the eggs are clean and that none of them have cracks. Inspect the eggs again once you get home and discard any that may have been damaged during transport.

• Inspect packaging on all foods. Make sure meat and poultry are tightly wrapped and fresh-cut vegetables are in sealed packages. Avoid canned food that have dents, rust, or bulges. Squeeze frozen foods to ensure they are frozen solid.

Prep Smart

• Wash all fresh produce—even if the label says "pre-washed"—before eating. Place greens in a large bowl of cold water and lift them out to drain in a colander. Place vegetables such as broccoli, cauliflower, green beans, and baby carrots in a colander and rinse under cold running water. Scrub sturdy produce such as apples, potatoes, and celery with a brush.

• Do not wash produce with soap or detergent. These products are not approved for use on food, and residues from them can be absorbed by the produce.

• Always marinate foods in the refrigerator. If you use the marinade to make a sauce, you must boil it first.

Clean Up

• Always wash your hands thoroughly before beginning any food preparation.

• Use hot soapy water and a dishcloth to clean kitchen countertops and appliances. Wash dishcloths and towels often in the washing machine using hot water.

On Board

• Keep two cutting boards: one for meats, poultry, and seafood and one for produce.

• Either wood or plastic cutting boards are acceptable to use. Wash them in hot soapy water after each use and dry thoroughly. To sanitize cutting boards, wash them with a solution of 1 tablespoon bleach in 1 gallon of water.

Thaw Safely

• **Slow and Sure:** Thawing in the refrigerator is the safest method of defrosting foods. Count on about 12 hours to thaw 1 pound of steak, ground beef, pork chops, chicken, or shrimp.

• **Faster:** You can thaw a 1-pound portion of food in about 2 hours in cold water. To do so, place the food in a zip-close plastic bag with a watertight seal. Submerge the bag in cold water and change the water every 30 minutes until the food is thawed. Cook the food immediately after thawing.

• **Fastest:** To thaw food in the microwave, follow the manufacturers' directions. The thawing time will depend on the amount of food and the wattage of your microwave. Cook any food thawed in the microwave immediately. Never thaw any food at room temperature.

Ginger Hoisin Burgers with Asian Slaw (5 POINTS VALUE)

level	technique	prep	cook	serves
Basic	Pan Sear pg. 20	15 min	10 min	4

- ◆ 1   pound ground lean beef (7% fat or less)
- ¼   cup plain dried bread crumbs
- ◆ ¼   cup thinly sliced scallions
- ¼   cup + 1 tablespoon hoisin sauce
- 2   tablespoons reduced-sodium soy sauce
- 1   tablespoon lime juice
- 1   tablespoon honey
- ◆ 4   cups thinly sliced Napa cabbage
- ◆ 4   radishes, shredded
- ◆ 1   carrot, shredded

1 Combine beef, bread crumbs, scallions, ¼ cup of hoisin sauce, and soy sauce in medium bowl, mixing just until combined. With damp hands, shape mixture into 4 (½-inch-thick) patties.

2 Spray medium nonstick skillet with nonstick spray and set over medium-high heat. Add patties and cook until instant-read thermometer inserted into side of each patty registers 160°F for medium, 5–6 minutes on each side.

3 Meanwhile, whisk together remaining 1 tablespoon hoisin sauce, lime juice, and honey in large bowl. Add cabbage, radishes, and carrot and toss to combine. Serve burgers with slaw.

PER SERVING (1 burger and 1 cup slaw): 252 Cal, 6 g Fat, 3 g Sat Fat, 0 g Trans Fat, 60 mg Chol, 745 mg Sod, 23 g Carb, 2 g Fib, 26 g Prot, 112 mg Calc.

IN THE KITCHEN

To cut prep time, use 4 cups packaged coleslaw mix instead of the cabbage, radishes, and carrot.

Minimum Safe Cooking Temperatures

• Use an instant-read thermometer to ensure that cooked foods are at a safe temperature.

• Insert the thermometer into the center of the food (without touching a bone in roasts or poultry) to get an accurate reading. Follow the minimum safe cooking temperatures in the chart below.

• Wash the stem of the thermometer with hot soapy water after each use.

TYPE OF FOOD	TEMPERATURE
Ground beef, pork, and lamb	160°F
Beef and lamb steaks, chops, or roasts	145°F (medium-rare) 160°F (medium)
Pork chops or roast	160°F
Fresh ham	160°F
Fully cooked ham (to reheat)	140°F
Chicken or turkey, whole, parts, or ground	165°
Egg dishes	160°F
Leftovers and casseroles	165°F

Italian Beef and Pasta Bake

level	technique	prep	cook	serves
Basic	Simmer pg. 22, Bake pg. 27	20 min	1 hr	8

- ♦ 3 cups whole wheat penne
- ♦ 1 pound ground lean beef (7% fat or less)
- ♦ 1 large onion, chopped
- 2 garlic cloves, minced
- ♦ 1 (28-ounce) can diced tomatoes
- 2 teaspoons dried oregano
- 1 teaspoon dried basil
- 3/4 teaspoon salt
- 1/2 teaspoon black pepper
- 1 cup part-skim ricotta cheese
- 1 cup shredded part-skim mozzarella cheese

1 Preheat oven to 350°F. Spray 9 x 13-inch baking dish with nonstick spray.

2 Cook penne according to package directions omitting salt, if desired. Drain and transfer to large bowl.

3 Meanwhile, cook beef, onion, and garlic in large nonstick skillet over medium-high heat, breaking up beef with wooden spoon, until beef is browned, about 8 minutes. Stir in tomatoes, oregano, basil, salt, and pepper; simmer, stirring occasionally, until sauce thickens slightly, about 15 minutes.

4 Stir beef mixture, ricotta, and 1/2 cup mozzarella into penne; transfer to baking dish. Sprinkle with remaining 1/2 cup mozzarella. Bake until heated through and lightly browned, about 25 minutes.

PER SERVING (about 1¼ cups): 348 Cal, 9 g Fat, 5 g Sat Fat, 0 g Trans Fat, 47 mg Chol, 671 mg Sod, 44 g Carb, 5 g Fib, 26 g Prot, 253 mg Calc.

IN THE KITCHEN

Serve this family-friendly casserole with a large tossed salad. Combine 8 cups torn romaine, 4 plum tomatoes, cut into wedges, 1 red bell pepper, cut into thin strips, and 1 small red onion, thinly sliced and toss with a drizzle of red-wine vinegar and salt and pepper to taste.

ITALIAN BEEF AND PASTA BAKE

Quick Takes Beef

Looking for something different to make tonight with ground beef? Grab **1 pound ground lean beef (7% fat or less)** and get cooking! Each recipe serves 4.

1 Ginger Beef In Lettuce Cups

Combine **3 tablespoons reduced-sodium soy sauce, 1 tablespoon grated peeled fresh ginger, 1 garlic clove, minced, and ⅛ teaspoon red pepper flakes.** Spray large nonstick skillet with nonstick spray and set over medium-high heat. Add **beef** and cook, breaking it apart with wooden spoon, until browned, about 3 minutes. Stir in **2 celery stalks, chopped,** and cook until crisp-tender, about 2 minutes. Add **½ cup sliced water chestnuts** and the soy sauce mixture; cook, stirring, until heated through, about 1 minute. Divide beef mixture among **8 large Boston lettuce leaves.** This recipe works with the **Simply Filling technique.**
PER SERVING (2 lettuce cups) *POINTS* value: **4.**

2 Moroccan Beef and Couscous

Spray large nonstick skillet with nonstick spray and set over medium-high heat. Add **beef, 2 garlic cloves, minced, and salt and black pepper to taste;** cook, breaking beef apart with wooden spoon, until browned, about 3 minutes. Add **1 (15-ounce) can diced tomatoes, undrained, ¾ pound green beans, trimmed and halved, 2 carrots, sliced, and ½ teaspoon dried oregano.** Simmer, covered, until flavors are blended, about 5 minutes. Serve with 1⅓ cups cooked couscous. This recipe works with the **Simply Filling technique.**
PER SERVING (¾ cup beef mixture and ⅓ cup couscous) *POINTS* value: **5.**

3 Succotash Chili

Spray large nonstick skillet with nonstick spray and set over medium-high heat. Add **beef, 1 small onion, chopped, 2 teaspoons chili powder, and salt to taste;** cook, breaking beef apart with wooden spoon, until browned, 3 minutes. Stir in **2 (10-ounce) packages frozen succotash, 1 (14½-ounce) can reduced-sodium chicken broth, 1 (4-ounce) can chopped mild green chiles, drained, and 1 tablespoon tomato paste.** Cook, stirring occasionally, until heated through, about 10 minutes. This recipe works with the **Simply Filling technique.**
PER SERVING (1 cup) *POINTS* value: **5.**

4 Southwestern Beef and Polenta

Spray large nonstick skillet with nonstick spray and set over medium-high heat. Slice **1 (16-ounce) tube refrigerated plain polenta** into 8 slices and put in skillet in a single layer; sprinkle with **salt and black pepper to taste.** Cook until browned, about 3 minutes on each side. Transfer to platter; keep warm. Add **beef** to the skillet and cook, breaking it apart with a wooden spoon, until browned, about 3 minutes. Stir in **1 (14-ounce) jar fat-free salsa and 1 (15½-ounce) can black beans, rinsed and drained;** cook until heated through, about 5 minutes. Spoon over the polenta. This recipe works with the **Simply Filling technique.**
PER SERVING (1 cup beef mixture and 2 slices polenta) *POINTS* value: **7.**

5 Jalapeño Burgers

Spray rack of broiler pan with nonstick spray and preheat the broiler. Combine **beef, 1 small onion, finely chopped, 1 jalapeño pepper, seeded and minced, 1 teaspoon dried mint, crushed, 1 teaspoon ground cumin, and ½ teaspoon salt** in medium bowl. Form into 4 (½-inch-thick) patties. Place patties on broiler rack and broil until instant-read thermometer inserted into side of each patty registers 160°F, about 5 minutes on each side. This recipe works with the **Simply Filling technique.**
PER SERVING (1 burger) *POINTS* value: **4.**

Big Red Beef Stew (7 POINTS VALUE)

level	technique	prep	cook	serves
Intermediate	Braise pg. 23	20 min	2 hr	4

- ♦ 1 (7-ounce) jar roasted red peppers (not in oil), drained
- ♦ 1 pound bottom round steak, trimmed and cut into 1-inch chunks
- ½ teaspoon salt
- ¼ teaspoon black pepper
- ♦ 1 large onion, chopped
- ♦ 1 celery stalk, chopped
- 3 garlic cloves, minced
- 1 teaspoon smoked sweet paprika
- ½ cup dry red wine
- ♦ 3 large carrots, halved lengthwise and cut into 2-inch pieces
- ♦ 1 (28-ounce) can diced tomatoes
- ♦ 8 ounces green beans, trimmed and cut into 1-inch pieces
- ♦ ½ cup frozen peas
- ¼ cup chopped fresh parsley
- ♦ 1 (16-ounce) tube fat-free polenta, cut into 12 slices

1 Preheat oven to 325°F. Put roasted peppers in food processor or blender and process until smooth.

2 Spray Dutch oven with nonstick spray and set over medium-high heat. Add beef and sprinkle with salt and pepper. Cook, stirring occasionally, until browned, about 4 minutes. Transfer to plate.

3 Add onion and celery to Dutch oven and cook, stirring occasionally, until softened and browned, 5 minutes. Add garlic and paprika and cook, stirring constantly, until fragrant, 30 seconds.

4 Add wine and simmer until it is almost evaporated, about 2 minutes. Add beef, carrots, tomatoes, and roasted peppers. Bring to simmer, cover, and transfer to oven. Bake until beef is very tender, about 1½ hours. Stir in beans and bake 10 minutes longer. Remove from oven, stir in peas and parsley, and let stand 10 minutes.

5 Meanwhile, spray broiler rack with nonstick spray and preheat broiler. Arrange slices of polenta on rack and broil 5 inches from heat until crispy and heated through, about 5 minutes on each side.

PER SERVING (1 cup stew with 3 slices polenta): 378 Cal, 6 g Fat, 2 g Sat Fat, 0 g Trans Fat, 84 mg Chol, 886 mg Sod, 42 g Carb, 8 g Fib, 40 g Prot, 138 mg Calc.

♦ FILLING EXTRA

You can double the amount of green beans and peas in the recipe.

Roasted Pork Tenderloin with Apple-Fig Sauce (5 POINTS VALUE)

level	technique	prep	cook	serves
Basic	Roast pg. 24	10 min	30 min	4

- ◆ 1 (1-pound) pork tenderloin, trimmed
- ½ teaspoon salt
- ¼ teaspoon black pepper
- ◆ 2 Granny Smith apples, cored, each cut into 8 wedges
- ¾ cup unsweetened apple cider
- 2 tablespoons fruit chutney (such as fig or apple)
- 8 dried black Mission figs, stemmed and quartered lengthwise
- 1 large shallot, minced
- 1 tablespoon chopped fresh parsley

1 Preheat oven to 400°F.

2 Spray large ovenproof skillet with nonstick spray and set over medium-high heat. Sprinkle tenderloin with salt and pepper; place in skillet and cook, turning occasionally, until browned on all sides, about 5 minutes.

3 Place apples around pork and transfer skillet to oven. Roast until an instant-read thermometer inserted into center of tenderloin registers 160°F for medium, about 15 minutes. Transfer pork to cutting board, cover loosely with foil, and let stand 10 minutes.

4 Place skillet over medium-high heat; add cider, chutney, figs, and shallot to apples. Cook, scraping up any browned bits on bottom of skillet, until juices are slightly thickened, about 6 minutes. Stir in parsley. Cut pork into 16 slices and serve with sauce.

PER SERVING (2 slices pork and ½ cup sauce): 258 Cal, 5 g Fat, 2 g Sat Fat, 0 g Trans Fat, 48 mg Chol, 373 mg Sod, 33 g Carb, 4 g Fib, 23 g Prot, 49 mg Calc.

IN THE KITCHEN

For this dish, the sauce is prepared in the same skillet where the pork baked. Be careful with the skillet when you make the sauce and don't inadvertently grasp the hot handle without a mitt.

Sage-Rubbed Pork Chops with Mushrooms

(5 POINTS VALUE)

level	technique	prep	cook	serves
Basic	Pan Sear pg. 20, Sauté pg. 18	10 min	15 min	4

◆ 4   (¼-pound) boneless center-cut pork loin chops, about ½ inch thick, trimmed

  1¼ teaspoons dried sage

  ³/4 teaspoon salt

  ½ teaspoon black pepper

  2 teaspoons olive oil

◆ 1 pound cremini mushrooms, quartered

  1 garlic clove, minced

  2 tablespoons chopped fresh flat-leaf parsley

1 Sprinkle pork chops with 1 teaspoon sage, ½ teaspoon salt, and ¼ teaspoon pepper.

2 Heat 1 teaspoon oil in large nonstick skillet over medium-high heat. Add chops to skillet and cook until instant-read thermometer inserted into side of each chop registers 160°F for medium, 3–4 minutes on each side. Transfer chops to platter; keep warm.

3 Add remaining 1 teaspoon oil to skillet. Add mushrooms, garlic, and remaining ¼ teaspoon sage, ¼ teaspoon salt, and ¼ teaspoon pepper. Cook, stirring occasionally, until mushrooms are tender, 6–8 minutes. Stir in parsley. Serve pork chops with mushrooms.

PER SERVING (1 pork chop with ½ cup mushrooms): 238 Cal, 11 g Fat, 4 g Sat Fat, 0 g Trans Fat, 72 mg Chol, 493 mg Sod, 5 g Carb, 1 g Fib, 28 g Prot, 33 mg Calc.

◆ FILLING EXTRA

Serve the pork chops with a baked sweet potato. One medium (5-ounce) baked sweet potato per serving will increase the **POINTS** value by **2**. This recipe works with the Simply Filling technique.

MEATLOAF WITH SHIITAKES AND CARAMELIZED ONIONS

Meatloaf with Shiitakes and Caramelized Onions (5 POINTS VALUE)

level	technique	prep	cook	serves
Intermediate	Sauté pg. 18, Bake pg. 27	15 min	1 hr 20 min	6

- 2 teaspoons olive oil
- ♦ 1 large onion, chopped
- 2 garlic cloves, minced
- ♦ 1/2 pound fresh shiitake mushrooms, stems discarded and caps sliced
- ♦ 1 1/2 pounds ground lean beef (7% fat or less)
- ♦ 1 cup tomato sauce
- 1/2 cup plain dried bread crumbs
- ♦ 2 large egg whites, lightly beaten
- 2 teaspoons Worcestershire sauce
- 1 teaspoon dried basil
- 1 teaspoon dried oregano
- 3/4 teaspoon salt
- 1/4 teaspoon black pepper

1 Preheat oven to 350°F. Spray large rimmed baking sheet with nonstick spray.

2 Meanwhile, heat 1 teaspoon oil in medium nonstick skillet over medium-high heat. Add onion and cook, stirring occasionally, until onion is tender and golden, about 10 minutes. Add garlic and cook, stirring constantly, until fragrant, 30 seconds. Transfer to large bowl. Add remaining 1 teaspoon oil to skillet. Add mushrooms and cook, stirring occasionally, until browned, 6–7 minutes. Add to bowl with onion; let cool 5 minutes.

3 Add beef, 1/2 cup tomato sauce, bread crumbs, egg whites, Worcestershire, basil, oregano, salt, and pepper to bowl and stir just until blended.

4 Transfer mixture to baking sheet and form into 4 x 9-inch loaf. Spread remaining 1/2 cup tomato sauce over top. Bake until instant-read thermometer inserted into center of loaf registers 160°F, about 1 hour. Let stand about 5 minutes before slicing. Cut into 12 slices.

PER SERVING (2 slices): 234 Cal, 7 g Fat, 3 g Sat Fat, 0 g Trans Fat, 60 mg Chol, 661 mg Sod, 15 g Carb, 3 g Fib, 26 g Prot, 45 mg Calc.

◆ FILLING EXTRA

To make an easy sauce for the meatloaf, simmer 1 1/2 cups tomato sauce in a small saucepan until heated through. Top each serving with 1/4 cup of the sauce. Serve with steamed green beans and yellow wax beans.

Grilled Pork with Tamarind Sauce

level	technique	prep	cook	serves
Basic	Grill pg. 26	15 min	15 min	4

2 tablespoons lime juice
2 tablespoons fish sauce
1 tablespoon packed brown sugar
1 teaspoon tamarind concentrate
2 tablespoons chopped fresh cilantro
1 garlic clove, minced
♦ 1 (1-pound) pork tenderloin, trimmed
¼ teaspoon salt
½ teaspoon coarsely ground black pepper

1 Spray grill rack with nonstick spray and preheat grill to medium-high or prepare medium-high fire.

2 To make tamarind sauce, whisk lime juice, fish sauce, brown sugar, and tamarind in small bowl until smooth. Stir in cilantro and garlic.

3 Sprinkle pork with salt and pepper. Place on grill rack and grill, turning frequently, until instant-read thermometer inserted into center of pork registers 160°F for medium, about 15 minutes. Transfer to cutting board, cover loosely with foil, and let stand 10 minutes. Cut pork into 16 slices and serve with sauce.

PER SERVING (4 slices pork with 1 tablespoon sauce): 151 Cal, 4 g Fat, 2 g Sat Fat, 0 g Trans Fat, 48 mg Chol, 897 mg Sod, 5 g Carb, 0 g Fib, 23 g Prot, 17 mg Calc.

IN THE KITCHEN

Tamarind is the fruit pod of a tall shade tree native to Asia. The flavor of the pulp is very complex: a heady mix of sweet and sour. Tamarind concentrate can be found in specialty and Middle Eastern food stores.

Quick Takes Pork

If you love pork and want supper on the table in a hurry, quick-cooking pork chops are a delicious option. To start, sprinkle 4 (¹⁄₄-pound) **boneless pork loin chops, trimmed,** with **salt and black pepper to taste,** then proceed as directed below. Each recipe serves 4.

1 Asian-Glazed Pork Chops

Whisk together **3 tablespoons honey, 2 tablespoons reduced-sodium soy sauce, 1 tablespoon balsamic vinegar,** and **¹⁄₂ teaspoon cornstarch** in small bowl. Spray large nonstick skillet with nonstick spray and set over medium-high heat. Add **pork** and cook until cooked through, 4–5 minutes on each side. Transfer to platter and keep warm. Add **1 garlic clove, minced,** to skillet and cook about 30 seconds. Stir in honey mixture and cook, stirring, about 1 minute. Pour over pork and sprinkle with **1 chopped scallion.**
PER SERVING (1 pork chop and 1¹⁄₂ tablespoons glaze) *POINTS* value: **5.**

2 Balsamic Pork Chops

Heat **2 teaspoons olive oil** in large nonstick skillet over medium-high heat. Add **pork** and cook until cooked through, 4–5 minutes on each side. Transfer to platter and keep warm. Add **2 shallots, minced,** to skillet and cook until softened, about 1 minute. Stir in **¹⁄₂ cup reduced-sodium chicken broth, ¹⁄₄ cup balsamic vinegar,** and **¹⁄₄ teaspoon dried thyme.** Cook until slightly reduced, about 4 minutes. Remove skillet from heat. Add 1 teaspoon butter, stirring until melted. Pour over pork.
PER SERVING (1 pork chop and about 2 tablespoons sauce) *POINTS* value: **5.**

3 Curried Pork Chops

Combine **1 tablespoon all-purpose flour** and **2 teaspoons curry powder** in medium bowl. Add **pork** and turn to coat. Heat **1 tablespoon canola oil** in large nonstick skillet over medium-high heat. Add pork and cook until cooked through, 4–5 minutes on each side. Sprinkle with **chopped fresh cilantro** and serve with **lemon wedges**.
PER SERVING (1 pork chop) *POINTS* value: **5.**

4 Pork Parmesan

Beat **1 large egg** in shallow dish. Spread **¹⁄₄ cup Italian-seasoned dried bread crumbs** on sheet of wax paper. Dip each **pork chop** in egg then in crumb mixture. Heat **1 tablespoon olive oil** in large nonstick skillet over medium-high heat. Add pork and cook until cooked through, 4–5 minutes on each side. Top evenly with **1 cup marinara sauce, heated, ¹⁄₂ cup shredded fat-free mozzarella** and **4 teaspoons grated Parmesan.**
PER SERVING (1 pork chop, ¹⁄₄ cup sauce, 2 tablespoons mozzarella, and 1 teaspoon Parmesan) *POINTS* value: **7.**

5 Pork with Cherries and Port

Heat **2 teaspoons olive oil** in large nonstick skillet over medium-high heat. Add **pork** and cook until cooked through, 4–5 minutes on each side. Transfer to platter and keep warm. Add **¹⁄₂ small red onion, finely chopped,** and **pinch dried thyme** to skillet; cook about 1 minute. Stir in **¹⁄₂ cup ruby port wine, ¹⁄₃ cup reduced-sodium chicken broth,** and **¹⁄₄ cup dried cherries.** Bring to boil; cook until reduced by half, about 3 minutes. Pour sauce over pork and sprinkle with **chopped fresh parsley.**
PER SERVING (1 pork chop and about 2 tablespoons sauce) *POINTS* value: **5.**

Pork and Peanut Stir-Fry (6 POINTS VALUE)

level	technique	prep	cook	serves
Basic	Stir-Fry pg. 19	10 min	10 min	4

- ♦ ¾ cup Chicken Stock (page 32) or store-bought reduced-sodium chicken broth
- ¼ cup dry sherry
- 3 tablespoons reduced-sodium soy sauce
- 1 tablespoon cornstarch
- 1 tablespoon chili-garlic paste
- 2 teaspoons canola oil
- ♦ 1 pound boneless center-cut pork loin chops, trimmed and thinly sliced
- ♦ 4 scallions, cut into 1-inch pieces
- 1 tablespoon minced peeled fresh ginger
- ♦ 3 cups broccoli florets

1 Whisk together stock, sherry, soy sauce, cornstarch, and chili-garlic paste in small bowl until smooth.

2 Heat large nonstick skillet or wok over medium-high heat until a drop of water sizzles on it. Pour in 1 teaspoon oil and swirl to coat pan; add pork and stir-fry until pork is cooked through, 4–5 minutes. Transfer to plate; cover to keep pork warm.

3 Heat remaining 1 teaspoon oil in same pan. Add scallions and ginger; stir-fry until fragrant, about 30 seconds. Add broccoli; stir-fry until crisp-tender, about 2 minutes. Re-whisk stock mixture; add to skillet and bring to boil. Reduce heat and simmer, stirring occasionally, until sauce bubbles and thickens slightly, about 2 minutes. Add pork and cook until heated through, about 1 minute.

PER SERVING (1 cup): 270 Cal, 12 g Fat, 3 g Sat Fat, 0 g Trans Fat, 72 mg Chol, 550 mg Sod, 12 g Carb, 3 g Fib, 28 g Prot, 52 mg Calc.

◆ FILLING EXTRA

Serve the stir-fry with cooked brown jasmine rice (½ cup cooked brown jasmine rice per serving will increase the **POINTS** value by **2**).

Horseradish-Glazed Grilled Ham
with Sweet Potatoes (6 POINTS VALUE)

level	technique	prep	cook	serves
Basic	Boil pg. 22, Grill pg. 26	10 min	30 min	4

- ◆ 2   large sweet potatoes (about ¾ pound each)
-    3   tablespoons packed brown sugar
-    2   tablespoons prepared horseradish
-    ¼   teaspoon black pepper
- ◆ 4   (¼-pound) slices reduced-sodium lean deli ham
- ◆ 1   large red onion, cut into 8 wedges

1 Spray grill rack with nonstick spray and preheat grill to medium-high or prepare medium-high fire.

2 Put potatoes in medium saucepan and add enough water to cover. Bring to boil over high heat; reduce heat and simmer, covered, just until almost tender, 20–25 minutes. Drain. When cool enough to handle, peel potatoes and quarter lengthwise.

3 Combine brown sugar, horseradish, and pepper in small bowl. Brush horseradish mixture on both sides of ham. Spray onion and potatoes with nonstick spray. Place on grill rack and grill, turning, until browned and tender, about 6 minutes. Meanwhile, place ham on grill rack and grill until heated through and browned, 2 minutes on each side.

PER SERVING (1 slice ham, 2 sweet potato wedges, and 2 onion wedges): 289 Cal, 6 g Fat, 2 g Sat Fat, 0 g Trans Fat, 60 mg Chol, 1,151 mg Sod, 32 g Carb, 3 g Fib, 25 g Prot, 55 mg Calc.

◆ FILLING EXTRA

Serve the ham and vegetables with a salad of finely shredded Savoy cabbage tossed with lime juice for a refreshing flavor counterpoint.

Apricot-Thyme Pork Loin with Port Wine Sauce (7 POINTS VALUE)

level	technique	prep	cook	serves
Intermediate	Roast pg. 24	15 min	1 hr 10 min	6

- ♦ 1 (1½-pound) boneless center-cut pork loin, trimmed
- 1 teaspoon dried thyme
- 1 teaspoon salt
- ¼ teaspoon black pepper
- ♦ 1 onion, chopped
- ♦ 1 carrot, chopped
- ♦ 2 cups Chicken Stock (page 32) or store-bought reduced-sodium chicken broth
- ⅔ cup ruby port
- 4 tablespoons apricot preserves
- ½ cup chopped dried apricots
- 1 tablespoon unsalted butter

1 Preheat oven to 400°F. Place rack in roasting pan and spray rack with nonstick spray.

2 Sprinkle pork with ¾ teaspoon thyme, ¾ teaspoon salt, and pepper and place on rack in roasting pan. Put onion, carrot, stock, and port in roasting pan.

3 Roast pork for 45 minutes. Brush pork with 1 tablespoon preserves and roast 5 minutes. Repeat roasting and brushing pork 3 more times with remaining 3 tablespoons preserves until instant-read thermometer inserted into center of pork registers 160°F for medium, about 15 minutes. Transfer pork to cutting board, cover loosely with foil, and let stand 10 minutes.

4 Meanwhile, to make sauce, strain pan juices through sieve into small saucepan. Discard solids. Add apricots and remaining ¼ teaspoon thyme to saucepan; bring to boil. Boil 1 minute. Remove pan from heat; swirl in butter and remaining ¼ teaspoon salt. Cut pork into 12 slices and serve with sauce.

PER SERVING (2 slices pork with 3 tablespoons sauce): 310 Cal, 11 g Fat, 4 g Sat Fat, 0 g Trans Fat, 78 mg Chol, 574 mg Sod, 23 g Carb, 2 g Fib, 28 g Prot, 31 mg Calc.

◆ FILLING EXTRA

Serve the pork with steamed carrots and asparagus, and mashed potatoes. To make the potatoes, peel 1½ pounds russet potatoes and cut into 1-inch pieces. Simmer in a saucepan in water until tender, 20 minutes. Drain and return to saucepan. Add ½ cup fat-free sour cream, 2 tablespoons fat-free milk, and ¼ teaspoon salt and mash (½ cup cooked mashed potatoes per serving will increase the **POINTS** value by **2**).

**APRICOT-THYME
PORK LOIN WITH
PORT WINE SAUCE**

Pizza with Peppers and Prosciutto

level	technique	prep	cook	serves
Basic	Bake pg. 27	25 min	25 min	6

	2	teaspoons olive oil
♦	8	plum tomatoes, chopped
	1	teaspoon sugar
	½	teaspoon dried oregano
	½	teaspoon dried basil
	¼	teaspoon salt
	1	tablespoon red-wine vinegar
	1	pound prepared fresh or thawed frozen pizza dough
♦	1	cup roasted red pepper (not in oil), thinly sliced
	8	thin slices prosciutto, cut into 1-inch strips (about 2 ounces)
	1	cup shredded part-skim mozzarella cheese

1 Place oven rack on bottom rung of oven. Preheat oven to 450°F.

2 Heat oil in large nonstick skillet over medium heat. Add tomatoes, sugar, oregano, basil, and salt; cook, stirring frequently, until most of liquid has evaporated, about 10 minutes. Stir in vinegar and cook 1 minute longer.

3 Spray 10½ x 15½-inch jelly-roll pan with nonstick spray. With floured hands, stretch and press pizza dough onto bottom of pan. Spread tomato sauce onto dough. Top crust evenly with roasted pepper and prosciutto. Sprinkle evenly with mozzarella.

4 Bake on bottom rack of oven until crust is golden and cheese is melted, 15–20 minutes. Cut into 6 squares.

PER SERVING (1 square): 301 Cal, 9 g Fat, 3 g Sat Fat, 0 g Trans Fat, 15 mg Chol, 632 mg Sod, 41 g Carb, 3 g Fib, 12 g Prot, 159 mg Calc.

Lamb Chops with Artichokes, Garlic, and Mint (3 POINTS VALUE)

level	technique	prep	cook	serves
Intermediate	Simmer pg. 22, Pan Sear pg. 20	15 min	15 min	4

- ♦ 1 pound baby artichokes (about 6), tough outer leaves discarded, each cut lengthwise in half
- ♦ 4 (5-ounce) bone-in loin lamb chops, about 1 inch thick, trimmed
- ¾ teaspoon salt
- ¼ teaspoon black pepper
- 2 garlic cloves, minced
- ½ cup dry white wine
- ♦ ½ cup Chicken Stock (page 32) or store-bought reduced-sodium chicken broth
- 2 tablespoons chopped fresh mint
- 1 tablespoon lemon juice

1 Bring large pot of water to boil over high heat. Add artichokes, reduce heat, and simmer until small knife inserted into bottom of an artichoke goes in easily, 10–15 minutes. Drain and keep warm.

2 Meanwhile, sprinkle lamb with ½ teaspoon salt and pepper. Spray large nonstick skillet with nonstick spray and set over medium-high heat. Add lamb and cook until instant-read thermometer inserted into side of each chop registers 145°F for medium, about 5 minutes on each side. Transfer to plate and keep warm.

3 Add garlic to skillet and cook, stirring constantly, until fragrant, 30 seconds. Add wine and cook, scraping up browned bits on bottom of skillet. Boil until wine is reduced to ¼ cup, about 1 minute. Add stock and return to boil; cook until liquid is reduced to about ½ cup. Stir in artichokes, mint, lemon juice, and remaining ¼ teaspoon salt.

4 Place chops on 4 plates. With slotted spoon, transfer artichokes evenly to plates. Drizzle chops and artichokes with pan juices.

PER SERVING (1 lamb chop and 3 artichoke halves): 153 Cal, 6 g Fat, 2 g Sat Fat, 0 g Trans Fat, 52 mg Chol, 556 mg Sod, 7 g Carb, 4 g Fib, 18 g Prot, 23 mg Calc.

IN THE KITCHEN

To save time, you can substitute a 14-ounce can quartered artichoke hearts, drained and halved for the fresh artichokes.

CHAPTER 6
Poultry

Chicken and turkey are sure bets for easy everyday meals. In this chapter you'll find creative new ways to cook these versatile and economical dinnertime standbys. Check out the Quick Takes, page 137 for super-simple meals that you can prepare in 20 minutes or less using skinless, boneless chicken breasts.

Cornmeal-Crusted Chicken Pot Pies

level	technique	prep	cook	serves
Intermediate	Simmer pg. 22, Bake pg. 27	35 min	45 min	6

- ◆ 2 cups Chicken Stock (page 32) or store-bought reduced-sodium chicken broth
- 2 teaspoons fresh thyme leaves
- ◆ ½ pound carrots, cut into ½-inch slices
- ◆ ½ pound red potatoes, cut into 1-inch chunks
- ◆ 3 celery stalks, cut into ½-inch slices
- ◆ ¾ pound green beans, cut into 2-inch lengths
- ◆ 1 cup frozen pearl onions, thawed
- ¾ cup all-purpose flour
- ◆ 3 cups shredded cooked chicken breast
- ¼ cup light sour cream
- ¾ teaspoon salt
- ½ teaspoon black pepper
- ¾ cup yellow cornmeal
- 1½ teaspoons baking powder
- ½ teaspoon baking soda
- 1 cup fat-free buttermilk
- ◆ 1 large egg
- 1½ tablespoons canola oil

1 Preheat oven to 400°F. Spray 6 (2-cup) ramekins or baking dishes with nonstick spray.

2 To make filling, combine stock and thyme in Dutch oven and bring to boil over high heat. Add carrots, potatoes, and celery; reduce heat and simmer 8 minutes. Add green beans and onions; simmer until vegetables are crisp-tender, about 4 minutes. Using slotted spoon, transfer vegetables to bowl and reserve.

3 Whisk ¼ cup flour into stock mixture until blended and bring to boil. Reduce heat and simmer, whisking constantly, until thickened, about 4 minutes. Stir in reserved vegetables, chicken, sour cream, ½ teaspoon salt, and pepper. Spoon filling into ramekins.

4 To make topping, whisk together cornmeal, remaining ½ cup flour, baking powder, baking soda, and remaining ¼ teaspoon salt in large bowl. Whisk buttermilk, egg, and oil in small bowl until blended. Add buttermilk mixture to cornmeal mixture, stirring to make a smooth batter. Spoon batter evenly over filling. Place the pot pies on a baking sheet for easy handling. Bake until crust is golden brown and filling is bubbly, about 25 minutes.

PER SERVING (1 potpie): 408 Cal, 10 g Fat, 3 g Sat Fat, 0 g Trans Fat, 98 mg Chol, 913 mg Sod, 49 g Carb, 6 g Fib, 31 g Prot, 204 mg Calc.

CORNMEAL-CRUSTED CHICKEN POT PIES

Sage and Orange Baked Chicken with Butternut Squash (5 POINTS VALUE)

level	technique	prep	cook	serves
Basic	Sauté pg. 18, Bake pg. 27	15 min	1 hr 10 min	8

- ♦ 1 onion, chopped
- ♦ 1 red bell pepper, chopped
- ♦ 1 medium butternut squash, seeded, peeled, and cut into ½-inch chunks
- 3 teaspoons chopped fresh sage
- 1 teaspoon salt
- ½ teaspoon black pepper
- ♦ 1 (4-pound) whole chicken, split in half and skinned
- 2 teaspoons grated orange zest
- ¼ cup orange juice

1 Preheat oven to 350°F. Spray 9 x 13-inch baking pan with nonstick spray.

2 Spray large nonstick skillet with nonstick spray and set over medium heat. Add onion and bell pepper; cook, stirring frequently, until slightly softened, about 3 minutes. Add squash; cook, stirring frequently, about 4 minutes. Stir in 1 teaspoon sage, ¼ teaspoon salt, and ¼ teaspoon black pepper. Arrange vegetables in pan.

3 Rub chicken with orange zest and remaining 2 teaspoons sage, ¾ teaspoon salt, and ¼ teaspoon black pepper. Place chicken over vegetables in pan.

4 Bake until vegetables are tender and instant-read thermometer inserted into thigh registers 180°F, about 1 hour. Transfer chicken to cutting board and let stand 10 minutes before carving. Stir orange juice into vegetables.

PER SERVING (⅛ of chicken with about ½ cup vegetables): 228 Cal, 7 g Fat, 2 g Sat Fat, 0 g Trans Fat, 81 mg Chol, 378 mg Sod, 14 g Carb, 2 g Fib, 28 g Prot, 63 mg Calc.

IN THE KITCHEN

If you don't have a thermometer, pierce the chicken with a fork and check the juices—they should be clear, not pink, when the chicken is cooked through.

Oven-Braised Chicken and Cremini Mushrooms

4 POINTS VALUE

level	technique	prep	cook	serves
Basic	Sauté pg. 18, Braise pg. 23	15 min	50 min	6

- ♦ 3 (3/4-pound) bone-in chicken breast halves, skinned and cut crosswise in half
- 1 teaspoon salt
- 1/4 teaspoon black pepper
- ♦ 1/2 pound cremini mushrooms, thinly sliced
- ♦ 1 small onion, chopped
- 1/2 cup dry white wine
- ♦ 1 cup Chicken Stock (page 32) or store-bought reduced-sodium chicken broth
- 1 tablespoon all-purpose flour
- 2 teaspoons chopped fresh rosemary or 1/2 teaspoon dried

1 Preheat oven to 375°F.

2 Sprinkle chicken with 3/4 teaspoon salt and 1/8 teaspoon pepper. Spray Dutch oven with nonstick spray and set over medium-high heat. Add chicken and cook until browned, about 2 minutes on each side. Transfer to plate.

3 Add mushrooms and onion and cook, stirring frequently, until vegetables are softened, 5 minutes. Add wine and cook until liquid is almost evaporated, about 3 minutes.

4 Whisk together stock and flour in bowl until smooth. Stir stock mixture into vegetable mixture; bring to boil. Stir in rosemary and remaining 1/4 teaspoon salt and 1/8 teaspoon pepper. Return chicken and any accumulated juices to Dutch oven.

5 Cover and bake until chicken is cooked through, about 35 minutes.

PER SERVING (1 chicken breast half with 1/3 cup mushroom sauce): 185 Cal, 4 g Fat, 1 g Sat Fat, 0 g Trans Fat, 74 mg Chol, 229 mg Sod, 5 g Carb, 1 g Fib, 29 g Prot, 23 mg Calc.

The Right Price

Chicken is one of the easiest and most economical of family dinners...if you shop right.

Bargain hunt There's no reason to buy chicken when it isn't on sale—most supermarkets have frequent chicken specials. Wait for a sale, stock up, and freeze it.

Don't be a skinless boneless chicken breast snob Chicken thighs are super cheap, and with just a little barbeque sauce they make a tasty meal. Chicken drumsticks, another bargain, are perfect for the slow cooker—they won't dry out even when cooked for hours.

Rotisserie rules Although precooked chickens are a bit more pricey, the value comes in time saved. A precooked rotisserie chicken will feed a family of four—but you can squeeze two meals out of one.

Less is more Limit the amount of chicken you serve and fill your plate with more veggies and whole grains instead—they're more economical and better for you. Add a nice green salad to the meal, and you'll be amazed at how little chicken you need to fill your plate.

Warm Chicken Salad with Goat Cheese Dressing ⑤ POINTS VALUE

level	technique	prep	cook	serves
Basic	Sauté pg. 18	15 min	10 min	6

- ⅓ cup fat-free mayonnaise
- ¼ cup crumbled goat cheese
- ♦ 3 tablespoons plain fat-free yogurt
- 2 teaspoons grated lemon zest
- 2 teaspoons lemon juice
- ♦ 6 (5-ounce) skinless boneless chicken breasts
- ½ teaspoon salt
- ⅛ teaspoon black pepper
- ♦ 4 cups torn Bibb lettuce leaves
- ♦ 1 cup cherry tomatoes
- ♦ 1 red bell pepper, seeded and thinly sliced
- ♦ ½ cucumber, peeled, seeded, and sliced
- ♦ ½ small red onion, thinly sliced

1 To make dressing, whisk together mayonnaise, goat cheese, yogurt, lemon zest, and lemon juice in medium bowl until smooth. Cover and refrigerate until ready to serve.

2 Sprinkle chicken with salt and pepper. Spray large nonstick skillet with nonstick spray and set over medium-high heat. Add chicken and cook, turning occasionally, until browned and cooked through, about 8 minutes. Transfer chicken to cutting board; let stand about 5 minutes, then cut each breast into thin slices.

3 Put lettuce, tomatoes, bell pepper, cucumber, and onion in large bowl and toss to combine. Divide lettuce mixture among 6 plates. Top salad evenly with chicken and drizzle with dressing.

PER SERVING (1½ cups salad with 1 chicken breast and 3 tablespoons dressing): 233 Cal, 7 g Fat, 2 g Sat Fat, 0 g Trans Fat, 92 mg Chol, 415 mg Sod, 7 g Carb, 2 g Fib, 35 g Prot, 64 mg Calc.

IN THE KITCHEN

Make a double batch of the dressing and store in the refrigerator up to 4 days. Use the dressing as a dip for vegetables or to drizzle over salads throughout the week.

Quick Takes Chicken

Chances are that skinless boneless chicken breast halves are your favorite part of the bird, so here's some new ways to enjoy them. Sprinkle 4 (5-ounce) **skinless boneless chicken breasts** with salt and black pepper to taste, then proceed as directed below. Each recipe serves 4.

1 Spiced Mint Chicken

Combine **$\frac{1}{2}$ cup chopped fresh mint, 1 tablespoon sesame seeds, 1 tablespoon fennel seeds, crushed, and 2 teaspoons dried thyme**; rub on chicken. Heat **2 teaspoons canola oil** in large nonstick skillet over medium-high heat. Add **chicken** and cook until cooked through, about 5 minutes on each side.
PER SERVING (1 chicken breast) *POINTS* value: **4.**

2 Cucumber-Yogurt Chicken

Combine **1 cup plain reduced-fat yogurt, 1 cup diced seedless cucumber, $\frac{1}{2}$ cup chopped radish, 2 tablespoons fat-free mayonnaise,** and **salt and black pepper to taste.** Sprinkle **chicken** with **1 tablespoon curry powder.** Spray ridged grill pan with nonstick spray; set over medium-high heat. Add chicken; cook until cooked through, about 5 minutes on each side. Serve with yogurt sauce.
PER SERVING (1 chicken breast and $\frac{1}{2}$ cup sauce) *POINTS* value: **4.**

3 Grilled Chicken Reubens

Preheat broiler. Spray ridged grill pan with nonstick spray; set over medium-high heat. Add **chicken** and cook until cooked through, about 5 minutes on each side. Meanwhile, combine **3 cups packaged coleslaw mix, $\frac{1}{4}$ cup chili sauce,** and **3 tablespoons fat-free mayonnaise** in a medium bowl. Place **4 slices toasted reduced-calorie rye bread** on the rack of broiler pan. Top each slice bread with 1 chicken breast. Spoon coleslaw mix evenly on top and cover each sandwich with **1 (1-ounce) slice fat-free Swiss cheese.** Broil until cheese melts, about 1 minute.
PER SERVING (1 sandwich) *POINTS* value: **5.**

4 Tangerine Chicken

Spray large nonstick skillet with nonstick spray; and set over medium-high heat. Add **chicken** and cook until cooked through, about 5 minutes on each side. Transfer to plate; keep warm. Stir together **$\frac{1}{3}$ cup reduced-sodium chicken broth** and **1 teaspoon cornstarch** in cup until smooth. Heat **1 tablespoon olive oil** in skillet. Add **2 chopped scallions**; cook about 1 minute. Stir in broth mixture and **3 peeled large tangerines, cut into sections and chopped,** along with their juice; cook about 2 minutes. Spoon over chicken.
PER SERVING (1 chicken breast and $\frac{1}{3}$ cup sauce) *POINTS* value: **5.**

5 Soft Chicken Tacos

Sprinkle **1 tablespoon chili powder** on **chicken.** Spray ridged grill pan with nonstick spray and set over medium-high heat. Add the chicken; cook until cooked through, about 5 minutes on each side. When cool enough to handle, cut on diagonal into strips. Warm **4 (8-inch) whole wheat tortillas** according to the package directions. Spoon one fourth of the chicken on each tortilla. Top evenly with **$\frac{1}{2}$ cup salsa, $\frac{1}{2}$ medium avocado,** diced, and **2 cups shredded lettuce.**
PER SERVING (1 taco) *POINTS* value: **6.**

CHICKEN WITH NOODLES AND VEGETABLES IN GINGER BROTH

Chicken with Noodles and Vegetables in Ginger Broth (7 POINTS VALUE)

level	technique	prep	cook	serves
Basic	Simmer pg. 22	15 min	25 min	4

- 4 ounces rice noodles
- ♦ 2 cups Chicken Stock (page 32) or store-bought reduced-sodium chicken broth
- 2 tablespoons reduced-sodium soy sauce
- 2 tablespoons honey
- 4 quarter-size slices peeled fresh ginger
- 3 star anise pods
- ♦ 4 (5-ounce) skinless boneless chicken breasts, thinly sliced
- ♦ 1 medium yellow squash, halved lengthwise and sliced
- ♦ 4 ounces snow peas, trimmed and halved
- 2 tablespoons chopped fresh cilantro

1 Cook rice noodles according to package directions; drain.

2 Meanwhile, combine stock, soy sauce, honey, ginger, and star anise in large skillet; bring to boil. Reduce heat, cover, and simmer about 5 minutes. Add chicken; return to simmer. Simmer, covered, for 10 minutes. Add yellow squash and peas and cook until chicken is cooked through and vegetables are crisp-tender, 5 minutes longer. Remove and discard ginger and star anise.

3 Divide noodles among 4 bowls. Top each bowl of noodles with 1 piece of chicken, and one quarter of stock and vegetable mixture. Sprinkle evenly with cilantro.

PER SERVING (1 bowl): 362 Cal, 6 g Fat, 2 g Sat Fat, 0 g Trans Fat, 88 mg Chol, 550 mg Sod, 39 g Carb, 2 g Fib, 37 g Prot, 49 mg Calc.

IN THE KITCHEN

You can vary this soup using any quick-cooking vegetables. Try substituting zucchini, green peas, shredded carrots, thinly sliced celery, or broccoli florets for the yellow squash and snow peas.

Grilled Chicken with Tomato-Zucchini Salad

level	technique	prep	cook	serves
Basic	Grill pg. 26	20 min	10 min	4

- 3 tablespoons fresh lime juice
- 2 tablespoons white-wine vinegar
- 1 tablespoon olive oil
- 2 garlic cloves, minced
- ◆ 4 (5-ounce) skinless boneless chicken breasts
- 1 teaspoon ground cumin
- 3/4 teaspoon salt
- ◆ 2 cups grape tomatoes, halved
- ◆ 1 medium zucchini, diced (about 1 1/2 cups)
- ◆ 1/2 small red onion, thinly sliced
- 3 tablespoons chopped fresh cilantro

1 Spray grill rack with nonstick spray. Preheat grill to medium-high or prepare medium-high fire.

2 Combine lime juice, vinegar, oil, and garlic in medium bowl. Transfer 3 tablespoons of mixture to zip-close plastic bag; add chicken and cumin. Squeeze out air and seal bag; turn to coat chicken. Refrigerate, turning bag occasionally, about 30 minutes. Reserve remaining marinade.

3 Remove chicken from marinade; discard marinade. Sprinkle chicken with 1/2 teaspoon salt. Place chicken on grill rack and grill, turning frequently, until chicken is cooked through, 8–10 minutes.

4 Meanwhile, to make salad, add tomatoes, zucchini, onion, cilantro, and remaining 1/4 teaspoon salt to reserved marinade and toss to coat. Serve chicken with salad.

PER SERVING (1 chicken breast with about 3/4 cup salad): 244 Cal, 8 g Fat, 2 g Sat Fat, 0 g Trans Fat, 88 mg Chol, 536 mg Sod, 7 g Carb, 2 g Fib, 34 g Prot, 44 mg Calc.

◆ FILLING EXTRA

To make a healthy side dish, stir 1 tablespoon lime juice and 1/2 teaspoon chili powder into 2 cups hot cooked brown rice (1/2 cup cooked brown rice for each serving will increase the **POINTS** value by **2**). This recipe works with the Simply Filling technique.

HOW TO...
Marinate Meats, Poultry, and Seafood

1

Put the marinade and the food to be marinated in a large zip-close plastic bag.

2

Squeeze out the air and seal the bag. Turn the bag to coat the food. Refrigerate for the time directed in the recipe, turning the bag occasionally. Always discard the marinade, unless the recipe instructs otherwise (for safety, marinades must be boiled first if they are incorporated into a dish).

Tea-Poached Chicken Fattoush Salad (6 POINTS VALUE)

level	technique	prep	cook	serves
Intermediate	Simmer pg. 22, Broil pg. 25	25 min	20 min	4

- ♦ 2 cups Chicken Stock (page 32) or store-bought reduced-sodium chicken broth
- 2 mint tea bags
- ♦ 4 (5-ounce) skinless boneless chicken breasts
- 2 tablespoons lemon juice
- 2 teaspoons olive oil
- 2 garlic cloves, minced
- ½ teaspoon ground coriander + extra for sprinkling
- ½ teaspoon ground cumin + extra for sprinkling
- ¼ teaspoon salt
- ¼ teaspoon black pepper
- 2 (6-inch) whole wheat pita breads
- ♦ 6 cups lightly packed torn frisée or Bibb lettuce
- ♦ 2 mini (Persian) seedless cucumbers, sliced
- ♦ 1 large tomato, cut into thin wedges
- ½ cup loosely packed fresh mint leaves

1 Combine stock and tea bags in large skillet and bring to boil over high heat. Reduce heat to low and simmer 5 minutes. Remove tea bags using slotted spoon and discard. Add chicken and cook, turning once, until cooked through, about 8 minutes. Transfer to cutting board and cut into bite-size pieces.

2 To make dressing, bring poaching liquid to boil over high heat and boil until reduced to ½ cup, 5 minutes; pour into large serving bowl. Whisk in lemon juice, oil, garlic, ½ teaspoon ground coriander, ½ teaspoon ground cumin, salt, and pepper.

3 Preheat broiler.

4 Lightly spray one side of each pita bread with olive oil nonstick spray, then sprinkle very lightly with remaining coriander and cumin. Arrange pita bread on broiler rack and broil 6 inches from heat until crisp, about 1 minute on each side. Let pita bread cool slightly, then cut into bite-size pieces.

5 Add chicken, pita, frisée, cucumbers, tomato, and mint to dressing and toss to coat.

PER SERVING (about 1¾ cups): 327 Cal, 9 g Fat, 2 g Sat Fat, 0 g Trans Fat, 88 mg Chol, 583 mg Sod, 23 g Carb, 5 g Fib, 39 g Prot, 97 mg Calc.

Middle Eastern Chicken Kebabs with Rice Pilaf (8 POINTS VALUE)

level	technique	prep	cook	serves
Intermediate	Simmer pg. 22, Grill pg. 26	10 min	55 min	4

KEBABS

- ♦ 1   pound skinless boneless chicken breasts, cut into 1-inch chunks
- 1   tablespoon lemon juice
- 1   teaspoon paprika
- ½   teaspoon each ground cumin and ground coriander
- ½   teaspoon salt

RICE

- 1   teaspoon olive oil
- ♦ 1   onion, finely chopped
- ♦ 1   cup brown basmati rice
- ♦ 2¼ cups Chicken Stock (page 32) or store-bought reduced-sodium chicken broth
- ¼   cup currants
- ½   teaspoon ground cumin
- ¼   teaspoon salt
- 1   tablespoon chopped fresh mint

1 To make kebabs, place chicken, lemon juice, paprika, cumin, and coriander in large zip-close plastic bag. Squeeze out air and seal bag; turn to coat chicken. Refrigerate, at least 1 hour or up to overnight.

2 To make rice, heat oil in medium saucepan over medium-high heat. Add onion and cook, stirring frequently, until softened, 3–5 minutes. Add rice and cook, stirring constantly, until lightly toasted, 2–3 minutes. Add stock, currants, cumin, and salt; bring to boil. Reduce heat and simmer, covered, until rice is tender, 40–45 minutes. Remove saucepan from heat. Let stand 10 minutes, then fluff rice with fork and stir in mint; keep warm.

3 Meanwhile, spray grill rack with olive oil nonstick spray. Preheat grill to medium-high or prepare medium-high fire. Thread chicken onto 4 (8-inch) metal skewers; sprinkle with ½ teaspoon salt. Place skewers on grill rack and grill chicken, turning frequently, until chicken is cooked through, 8–10 minutes. Serve with rice.

PER SERVING (1 skewer and ¾ cup rice): 388 Cal, 7 g Fat, 2 g Sat Fat, 0 g Trans Fat, 70 mg Chol, 724 mg Sod, 47 g Carb, 7 g Fib, 33 g Prot, 56 mg Calc.

**MIDDLE EASTERN
CHICKEN KEBABS
WITH RICE PILAF**

Chicken and Black Bean Chili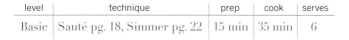

level	technique	prep	cook	serves
Basic	Sauté pg. 18, Simmer pg. 22	15 min	35 min	6

2	teaspoons canola oil
♦ 1	pound skinless boneless chicken breasts, cut into 1-inch pieces
♦ 1	large onion, chopped
♦ 1	large red bell pepper, diced
2	garlic cloves, minced
1	tablespoon chili powder
2	teaspoons ground cumin
1	(16-ounce) jar mild picante sauce
♦ 1	(15$\frac{1}{2}$-ounce) can black beans, rinsed and drained
$\frac{1}{2}$	cup water

1 Heat oil in Dutch oven over medium-high heat. Add chicken and cook, stirring often, until lightly browned, about 5 minutes. Add onion and bell pepper and cook, stirring often, until vegetables are softened, about 5 minutes. Add garlic, chili powder, and cumin and cook, stirring constantly, until fragrant, 30 seconds.

2 Stir in picante sauce, beans, and water; bring to boil. Reduce heat and simmer, partially covered, about 20 minutes.

PER SERVING (generous 1 cup chili): 225 Cal, 5 g Fat, 1 g Sat Fat, 0 g Trans Fat, 47 mg Chol, 704 mg Sod, 23 g Carb, 8 g Fib, 23 g Prot, 83 mg Calc.

♦ FILLING EXTRA

Top the chili with shredded fat-free Cheddar cheese, thinly sliced scallions, and chopped fresh cilantro. This recipe works with the Simply Filling technique.

Gingery Chicken Stir-Fry with Snow Peas and Peppers ⑤ POINTS VALUE

level	technique	prep	cook	serves
Basic	Stir-Fry pg. 19	10 min	10 min	4

♦ ²⁄₃ cup Chicken Stock (page 32) or store-bought reduced-sodium chicken broth

3 tablespoons oyster sauce

1 tablespoon reduced-sodium soy sauce

1 tablespoon cornstarch

4 teaspoons Asian (dark) sesame oil

♦ 1 pound skinless boneless chicken breasts, cut into thin strips

♦ 1 large red bell pepper, thinly sliced

♦ ¼ pound snow peas, trimmed

♦ 2 scallions, cut into 1-inch pieces

1 tablespoon grated peeled fresh ginger

1 Whisk together stock, oyster sauce, soy sauce, and cornstarch in small bowl until smooth.

2 Heat large nonstick skillet or wok over medium-high heat until a drop of water sizzles on it. Pour in 2 teaspoons oil and swirl to coat pan. Add chicken and stir-fry until chicken is browned and cooked through, about 4 minutes. Transfer chicken to plate.

3 Heat remaining 2 teaspoons oil in same pan. Add bell pepper, peas, scallions, and ginger; stir-fry until vegetables are crisp-tender, about 2 minutes. Add chicken to pan. Re-whisk stock mixture and add to pan. Cook, stirring constantly, until mixture bubbles and thickens, about 1 minute.

PER SERVING (¾ cup): 236 Cal, 9 g Fat, 2 g Sat Fat, 0 g Trans Fat, 70 mg Chol, 591 mg Sod, 10 g Carb, 2 g Fib, 28 g Prot, 39 mg Calc.

◆ FILLING EXTRA

Serve this stir-fry over whole wheat spaghetti to make a complete meal (¾ cup of cooked whole wheat spaghetti per serving will increase the **POINTS** value by **2**).

Coffee-Braised Chicken Thighs ④ POINTS VALUE

level	technique	prep	cook	serves
Basic	Sauté pg. 18, Simmer pg. 22	10 min	40 min	4

- ◆ 4 (5-ounce) skinless bone-in chicken thighs
- ½ teaspoon salt
- ⅛ teaspoon black pepper
- ◆ 1 medium onion, halved and sliced
- 2 garlic cloves, thinly sliced
- 1 teaspoon fennel seeds
- 1 teaspoon ancho chile powder
- 1 teaspoon dried oregano
- 1 teaspoon packed brown sugar
- ¾ cup strong brewed coffee
- 2 teaspoons balsamic vinegar

1 Sprinkle chicken with salt and pepper. Spray large deep nonstick skillet with nonstick spray and set over medium-high heat. Add chicken and cook, turning once, until browned, about 6 minutes. Transfer to plate.

2 Add onion, garlic, fennel seeds, chile powder, oregano, and brown sugar to skillet and stir to blend. Reduce heat to low, cover, and cook, stirring occasionally, until onion is tender, 8 minutes. Add coffee and vinegar and bring to boil.

3 Place chicken thighs on top of onion mixture. Reduce heat to low, cover, and simmer 10 minutes. Turn chicken thighs and simmer until chicken is tender and cooked through, about 10 minutes.

PER SERVING (1 chicken thigh and 3 tablespoons sauce): 172 Cal, 8 g Fat, 2 g Sat Fat, 0 g Trans Fat, 57 mg Chol, 355 mg Sod, 6 g Carb, 1 g Fib, 20 g Prot, 44 mg Calc.

◆ FILLING EXTRA

Serve this saucy chicken dish with brown rice (½ cup cooked brown rice with each serving will increase the *POINTS* value by *2*).

Bird in a Box

When time is tight, a rotisserie chicken is a cook's secret weapon. You can serve the bird as is with a few sides or carve it and use the meat in soups, salads, and sandwiches. Follow these golden rules to choose the best bird on the spit.

Rule 1: Avoid purchasing birds that are kept in hot boxes, displayed under heat lamps, or packed in containers or tightly wrapped in plastic. If the bird appears shrunken, chances are good the meat is dry. Always ask the server to give you the most recently roasted bird.

Rule 2: Shop at individually-owned stores (or, in some cases, small chains) that cook and serve their birds right away. The ideal scenario is to purchase chickens that are cooked in the store.

Rule 3: Shop early when possible so you won't have to purchase birds that have been on the rotisserie all day. Even better, shop for your rotisserie bird when the store is operating at peak busy hours (the manager will want to have plenty of fresh birds in stock during this time).

Chicken and White Bean Stew with Lemon and Sage (6 POINTS VALUE)

level	technique	prep	cook	serves
Basic	Sauté pg. 18, Simmer pg. 22	20 min	35 min	4

◆ 4   (5-ounce) skinless bone-in chicken thighs
½   teaspoon salt
¼   teaspoon black pepper
2   teaspoons olive oil
◆ 1   large onion, chopped
3   garlic cloves, minced
1   tablespoon all-purpose flour
◆ 1   (14½-ounce) can diced tomatoes
◆ ¾   cup Chicken Stock (page 32) or store-bought reduced-sodium chicken broth
◆ 1   (15½-ounce) can cannellini (white kidney) beans, rinsed and drained
1   tablespoon minced fresh sage or 1 teaspoon dried
2   teaspoons grated lemon zest

1 Sprinkle chicken with salt and pepper. Heat oil in Dutch oven over medium-high heat. Add chicken and cook, turning once, until browned, about 6 minutes. Transfer to plate. Add remaining 1 teaspoon oil to Dutch oven. Add onion and cook, stirring occasionally, until softened, about 5 minutes. Add garlic and cook, stirring constantly, until fragrant, 30 seconds.

2 Add flour and cook, stirring constantly, until it browns slightly, about 1 minute. Add tomatoes and stock; bring to boil, stirring constantly to scrape browned bits from bottom of pot. Add chicken, beans, and sage. Reduce heat and simmer, covered, until chicken is tender and cooked through, about 20 minutes. Stir in lemon zest.

PER SERVING (1 chicken thigh with about 1 cup bean mixture): 322 Cal, 10 g Fat, 3 g Sat Fat, 0 g Trans Fat, 57 mg Chol, 793 mg Sod, 29 g Carb, 7 g Fib, 29 g Prot, 138 mg Calc.

◆ FILLING EXTRA

Serve the stew with a side dish of steamed Swiss chard.

**CHICKEN AND BLACK BEAN
MOLE TOSTADAS**

Chicken and Black Bean Mole Tostadas (7 POINTS VALUE)

level	technique	prep	cook	serves
Basic	Sauté pg. 18, Simmer pg. 22	15 min	20 min	4

8 (6-inch) corn tortillas
1 teaspoon canola oil
♦ 1 large onion, chopped
2 garlic cloves, minced
1 tablespoon unsweetened cocoa powder
1 teaspoon ancho chile powder
1 teaspoon ground cumin
½ teaspoon cinnamon
½ teaspoon salt
½ teaspoon sugar
½ teaspoon dried oregano
♦ 1 (14½-ounce) can diced tomatoes
♦ 1 (15½-ounce) can black beans, rinsed and drained
♦ 1 cup shredded cooked chicken breast
♦ 2 cups shredded romaine lettuce
♦ 1 large tomato, chopped

1 Preheat oven to 425°F. Lightly spray large baking sheet with nonstick spray.

2 Arrange tortillas in single layer on baking sheet and lightly spray with nonstick spray. Bake until crisp, 6–8 minutes. Transfer tortillas to wire rack to cool.

3 Meanwhile, heat oil in large nonstick skillet over medium heat. Add onion and garlic; cook, stirring frequently, until golden, about 7 minutes. Add cocoa, chile powder, cumin, cinnamon, salt, sugar, and oregano; cook, stirring constantly, until fragrant, about 1 minute.

4 Add tomatoes, beans, and chicken; bring to boil. Reduce heat and simmer, stirring occasionally, until thickened, 10–12 minutes.

5 Spoon about ⅓ cup of chili onto each of tortillas. Top evenly with lettuce and tomato.

PER SERVING (2 tostadas): 340 Cal, 6 g Fat, 1 g Sat Fat, 0 g Trans Fat, 28 mg Chol, 846 mg Sod, 54 g Carb, 14 g Fib, 22 g Prot, 165 mg Calc.

Honey-Herb Roast Turkey Breast with Pan Gravy (4 POINTS VALUE)

level	technique	prep	cook	serves
Intermediate	Roast pg. 24, Simmer pg. 22	20 min	2 hr 10 min	10

- 2 tablespoons honey
- 2 tablespoons chopped fresh sage
- 1 tablespoon chopped fresh thyme
- 1 tablespoon light butter
- 1 teaspoon Dijon mustard
- ♦ 1 (4½-pound) turkey breast with ribs
- ½ teaspoon salt
- ¼ teaspoon black pepper
- ♦ 4 cups Chicken Stock (page 32) or store-bought reduced-sodium chicken broth
- 2 tablespoons all-purpose flour

1 Preheat oven to 375°F. Spray large roasting pan with nonstick spray.

2 Stir honey, sage, thyme, butter, and mustard together in small bowl. Loosen skin around turkey breast by running your fingers between skin and meat, starting at tips of breast halves. Once skin is loosened, spread most of honey mixture on meat, patting skin back in place. Rub remaining honey mixture all over skin; sprinkle evenly with salt and pepper.

3 Place turkey breast in pan. Pour 1½ cups of stock into pan. Roast turkey until instant-read thermometer inserted into center registers 165°F, 2 hours. Transfer turkey breast to cutting board, cover loosely with foil, and let stand 10 minutes.

4 Meanwhile, to make gravy, pour pan juices into measuring cup and skim off any fat; return juices to pan. Whisk remaining 2½ cups stock and flour in small bowl until smooth; add to roasting pan. Set pan over two burners over medium-high heat; cook, whisking constantly, until mixture comes to boil. Reduce heat and simmer, whisking occasionally, until gravy is reduced to 2 cups, about 3 minutes.

5 Discard ribs and skin from turkey breast. Cut turkey into 20 slices and serve with gravy.

PER SERVING (2 slices turkey and about 1½ tablespoons gravy): 211 Cal, 3 g Fat, 1 g Sat Fat, 0 g Trans Fat, 107 mg Chol, 353 mg Sod, 6 g Carb, 0 g Fib, 39 g Prot, 26 mg Calc.

Turkey Cutlets with Lemon (3 POINTS VALUE)

level	technique	prep	cook	serves
Basic	Sauté pg. 18	15 min	10 min	4

- ♦ 3   Meyer or regular lemons
- 2   tablespoons all-purpose flour
- ¼   teaspoon salt
- ¼   teaspoon black pepper
- ♦ 4   (¼-pound) turkey breast cutlets
- 2   teaspoons light butter
- 1   teaspoon sugar
- ♦ ½   cup Chicken Stock (page 32) or store-bought reduced-sodium chicken broth
- 2   fresh thyme sprigs or ½ teaspoon dried thyme

1 With vegetable peeler, remove zest from lemons in wide strips. With small knife, scrape off any white pith from underside of strips. Cut zest lengthwise into thin strips. Remove all white pith from lemons and cut into sections (if using regular lemons, section 1 lemon and reserve remaining lemons for another use).

2 On sheet of wax paper, combine flour, salt, and pepper. Lightly coat turkey with flour mixture.

3 Spray large nonstick skillet with nonstick spray and set over medium heat. Add turkey and cook, turning once, until golden brown and almost cooked through, about 3 minutes. Transfer to plate.

4 Add butter to skillet and reduce heat to low. Add lemon zest and sugar; cook, stirring frequently, until zest is lightly browned, about 3 minutes. Transfer to paper towel to drain.

5 Add stock and thyme to skillet; bring to boil over medium-high heat. Add turkey and lemon sections to skillet; simmer until turkey is cooked through, about 2 minutes longer. Serve turkey with sauce; sprinkle evenly with zest.

PER SERVING (1 turkey cutlet with about 1½ tablespoons sauce): 162 Cal, 2 g Fat, 1 g Sat Fat, 0 g Trans Fat, 78 mg Chol, 255 mg Sod, 7 g Carb, 1 g Fib, 28 g Prot, 27 mg Calc.

IN THE KITCHEN

Meyer lemons are thought to be a cross between a lemon and a Mandarin orange. They're sweeter than regular lemons with an intoxicating floral aroma. They are usually available during the winter months.

Turkey Meatball Hero Sandwiches

level	technique	prep	cook	serves
Intermediate	Simmer pg. 22	20 min	20 min	4

- ◆ 1 cup sun-dried tomatoes (not oil-packed)
- ◆ 1 cup Homemade Marinara Sauce (page 34) or store-bought tomato sauce
- 1 cup fresh basil leaves
- ◆ 2/3 cup Chicken Stock (page 32) or store-bought reduced-sodium chicken broth
- ◆ 1 pound ground skinless turkey breast
- 1/3 cup plain dried bread crumbs
- 1/3 cup grated Parmesan cheese
- ◆ 1 large egg white
- 1/4 teaspoon black pepper
- 4 (2-ounce) whole wheat hero rolls, toasted
- 1/2 cup shredded part-skim mozzarella cheese

1 Combine sun-dried tomatoes and enough boiling water to cover in medium bowl. Let stand until softened, about 10 minutes; drain.

2 Put sun-dried tomatoes, marinara sauce, basil, and stock in blender and puree.

3 Stir together turkey, bread crumbs, Parmesan, egg white, and pepper in large bowl; shape into 20 meatballs.

4 Spray large nonstick skillet with nonstick spray and set over medium-high heat. Add meatballs and cook, turning occasionally, until browned, about 4 minutes. Add sun-dried tomato mixture and bring to boil. Reduce heat and simmer, covered, until meatballs are cooked through, 8–10 minutes.

5 Fill rolls evenly with meatballs and sauce; sprinkle evenly with mozzarella.

PER SERVING (1 sandwich): 447 Cal, 10 g Fat, 4 g Sat Fat, 0 g Trans Fat, 90 mg Chol, 1164 mg Sod, 43 g Carb, 7 g Fib, 47 g Prot, 359 mg Calc.

◆ FILLING EXTRA

Serve the sandwich with a side of carrot and celery sticks for extra crunch and color.

**TURKEY MEATBALL
HERO SANDWICHES**

Cuban-Style Sloppy Joes (4 POINTS VALUE)

level	technique	prep	cook	serves
Basic	Sauté pg. 18, Simmer pg. 22	15 min	25 min	6

- ♦ 1 large onion, diced
- 3 garlic cloves, minced
- ♦ 1 red bell pepper, cut into 1/2-inch pieces
- ♦ 1 yellow bell pepper, cut into 1/2-inch pieces
- 2 teaspoons ground cumin
- ♦ 1 pound ground skinless turkey breast
- ♦ 3/4 cup Homemade Marinara Sauce (page 34) or tomato sauce
- 1/2 cup chili sauce
- 2 tablespoons dried currants
- ♦ 6 small pimiento-stuffed green olives, rinsed and sliced
- 1/2 teaspoon red pepper flakes
- 6 whole wheat potato rolls, split and toasted

1 Spray large nonstick skillet with nonstick spray and set over medium heat. Add onion and garlic; cook, stirring, until onion begins to soften, about 3 minutes. Add bell peppers and cumin; cook, stirring, until peppers soften, about 3 minutes. Add turkey and cook, breaking it up with wooden spoon, until no longer pink, about 5 minutes.

2 Add marinara sauce, chili sauce, currants, olives, and pepper flakes, stirring to combine; bring mixture to simmer. Reduce heat to low and simmer, covered, stirring occasionally, until thickened, about 12 minutes. Spoon 3/4 cup of turkey mixture onto bottom of each roll. Cover with tops of rolls.

PER SERVING (1 sandwich): 246 Cal, 3 g Fat, 1 g Sat Fat, 0 g Trans Fat, 51 mg Chol, 664 mg Sod, 29 g Carb, 6 g Fib, 24 g Prot, 88 mg Calc.

♦ FILLING EXTRA

Top the sandwiches with thinly sliced cabbage for extra crunch and color.

Spinach and Nut-Stuffed Cornish Hens (6 POINTS VALUE)

level	technique	prep	cook	serves
Intermediate	Bake pg. 27	15 min	1 hr 15 min	4

- 3 tablespoons maple syrup
- 2 teaspoons melted butter
- ♦ 1 (10-ounce) package frozen chopped spinach, thawed and squeezed dry
- ♦ 1 large Gala apple, peeled and chopped
- ¼ cup pine nuts, toasted (see box at right)
- ♦ 2 tablespoons chopped scallions
- ½ teaspoon salt
- ¼ teaspoon black pepper
- ♦ 2 (1¼-pound) Cornish game hens, skinned

1 Preheat oven to 350°F. Place rack in roasting pan.

2 Stir together 2 tablespoons maple syrup and butter in small bowl.

3 To make stuffing, stir together remaining 1 tablespoon maple syrup, spinach, apple, pine nuts, scallions, salt, and pepper in medium bowl. Spoon half of stuffing into cavity of each hen. Tie legs of each hen together with kitchen string.

4 Place hens on rack in roasting pan. Brush hens with some of syrup mixture. Bake, basting every 15 minutes with syrup mixture, until instant-read thermometer inserted into a thigh registers 180°F, about 1 hour 15 minutes.

5 Transfer hens to cutting board, cover loosely with foil and let stand 5 minutes. Pour pan juices into measuring cup and skim off any fat. Cut each hen in half and serve with pan juices.

PER SERVING (½ stuffed hen with 2 teaspoons pan juices): 304 Cal, 12 g Fat, 3 g Sat Fat, 0 g Trans Fat, 122 mg Chol, 425 mg Sod, 21 g Carb, 3 g Fib, 29 g Prot, 104 mg Calc.

♦ FILLING EXTRA

Quinoa makes a quick accompaniment to the hens (½ cup cooked quinoa per serving will increase the **POINTS** value by **2**).

HOW TO...
Toast Nuts

1

To get the best flavor from nuts, try toasting them. Preheat the oven or toaster oven to 350°F. Spread the nuts in a shallow baking pan.

2

Bake, shaking the pan often, until the nuts are lightly browned and fragrant, about 8 minutes. To keep their crunchy texture, sprinkle them on whatever you are serving at the last minute.

CHAPTER 7

Seafood

Fish and shellfish are extremely healthful and relatively low in calories. If the thought of preparing creatures of the sea intimidates you, this chapter will help you see that they can be very easy to cook. Buy seafood that's fresh, don't overcook it, and you'll have delicious results.

Grilled Salmon with Orchard Fruit Salad ⑥

level	technique	prep	cook	serves
Basic	Grill pg. 26	15 min	10 min	4

- ♦ 2 tablespoons minced red onion
- 1 tablespoon apple cider vinegar
- 1 tablespoon lemon juice
- 2 teaspoons molasses
- 1 teaspoon olive oil
- ½ teaspoon salt
- ♦ 4 (5-ounce) salmon fillets
- ⅛ teaspoon black pepper
- ♦ 4 cups mixed baby salad greens
- ♦ 1 ripe pear, thinly sliced
- ♦ 1 apple, thinly sliced

1 Spray grill rack with nonstick spray. Preheat grill to medium-high or prepare medium-high fire.

2 To make dressing, whisk together onion, vinegar, lemon juice, molasses, oil, and ¼ teaspoon salt in large bowl.

3 Sprinkle salmon with remaining ¼ teaspoon salt and pepper. Place on grill rack and grill, turning once, until salmon is just opaque in center, 8–10 minutes.

4 Add greens, pear, and apple to dressing and toss to coat. Divide salad evenly among 4 plates and top each with salmon fillet.

PER SERVING (1 salmon fillet with 1½ cups salad): 284 Cal, 9 g Fat, 2 g Sat Fat, 0 g Trans Fat, 93 mg Chol, 399 mg Sod, 18 g Carb, 4 g Fib, 31 g Prot, 59 mg Calc.

◆ FILLING EXTRA

For extra flavor, add 1 or 2 chopped plums to the salad.

**GRILLED SALMON WITH
ORCHARD FRUIT SALAD**

Salmon with Mango-Ginger Salsa

level	technique	prep	cook	serves
Basic	Pan Sear pg. 20	15 min	10 min	4

- ♦ 1 large mango, peeled, pitted, and chopped
- ♦ 1 small red bell pepper, diced
- ♦ 1 jalapeño pepper, seeded and minced
- ♦ 2 tablespoons diced red onion
-   1 tablespoon fresh lime juice
-   1 tablespoon chopped fresh cilantro
-   2 teaspoons grated peeled fresh ginger
- ♦ 4 (5-ounce) salmon fillets
-   ¼ teaspoon salt
-   ⅛ teaspoon black pepper

1 To make salsa, gently stir together mango, bell pepper, jalapeño, onion, lime juice, cilantro, and ginger in medium bowl.

2 Spray large nonstick skillet with nonstick spray and set over medium-high heat. Sprinkle salmon with salt and pepper. Place salmon in skillet and cook until just opaque in center, about 4 minutes on each side. Serve salmon with salsa.

PER SERVING (1 salmon fillet with ½ cup salsa): 248 Cal, 8 g Fat, 2 g Sat Fat, 0 g Trans Fat, 93 mg Chol, 235 mg Sod, 11 g Carb, 2 g Fib, 31 g Prot, 26 mg Calc.

♦ FILLING EXTRA

Serve the salmon with green beans. To cook them in the microwave, put 4 cups trimmed green beans in a microwavable dish and add 2 tablespoons water. Cover with wax paper and microwave on High until crisp-tender, about 4 minutes. This recipe works with the Simply Filling technique.

Poached Salmon with Dilled Yogurt

level	technique	prep	cook	serves
Basic	Simmer pg. 22	10 min	30 min	4

- ♦ 2 cups Vegetable Stock (page 30) or store-bought reduced-sodium vegetable broth
- 1 cup dry white wine
- ♦ 1 medium onion, thinly sliced
- 1 lemon, thinly sliced
- 4 dill sprigs
- ½ teaspoon salt
- 1 bay leaf
- ♦ 4 (5-ounce) salmon fillets
- ♦ ½ cup plain fat-free Greek-style yogurt
- 1 tablespoon chopped fresh dill
- 1 tablespoon minced scallion
- 1 teaspoon grated lemon zest

1 Combine stock, wine, onion, lemon, dill sprigs, salt, and bay leaf in large deep skillet; bring to boil over medium-high heat. Reduce heat to medium-low and return to simmer; cook, uncovered, 10 minutes. Carefully place salmon in broth; simmer, covered, until salmon is just opaque in center, about 10 minutes. With spatula, carefully transfer salmon to 4 serving plates. Discard stock mixture.

2 Meanwhile, to make sauce, stir together yogurt, chopped dill, scallion, and lemon zest in small bowl. Serve salmon with sauce.

PER SERVING (1 salmon fillet with 2 tablespoons sauce): 228 Cal, 8 g Fat, 2 g Sat Fat, 0 g Trans Fat, 94 mg Chol, 232 mg Sod, 4 g Carb, 0 g Fib, 32 g Prot, 87 mg Calc.

IN THE KITCHEN

You can use fresh basil, cilantro, or flat-leaf parsley instead of the dill.

**TUNA WITH GRAPEFRUIT-
AVOCADO RELISH**

Tuna with Grapefruit-Avocado Relish

level	technique	prep	cook	serves
Basic	Pan Sear pg. 20	10 min	10 min	4

- ♦ 2 ruby grapefruits, peeled and cut into sections
- ♦ 1 small avocado, peeled, pitted, and cut into ½-inch pieces
- ♦ 2 scallions, thinly sliced
-   ¼ cup chopped fresh flat-leaf parsley
- ♦ 4 (5-ounce) tuna steaks
-   ½ teaspoon salt
-   ⅛ teaspoon black pepper

1 To make relish, place grapefruit sections in medium bowl; break into small pieces using 2 forks. Stir in avocado, scallions, and parsley.

2 Spray large nonstick skillet with nonstick spray and set over medium-high heat. Sprinkle tuna with salt and pepper. Place tuna in pan and cook until just slightly pink in center, 3 minutes on each side. Serve tuna with relish.

PER SERVING (1 tuna steak and about ½ cup relish): 279 Cal, 11 g Fat, 2 g Sat Fat, 0 g Trans Fat, 90 mg Chol, 485 mg Sod, 13 g Carb, 5 g Fib, 34 g Prot, 75 mg Calc.

IN THE KITCHEN

Tuna is best when cooked until it is still pink in the center to prevent it from drying out. If you prefer, substitute salmon or halibut fillets and cook until just opaque in the center. This recipe works with the Simply Filling technique.

Mediterranean Wheat Berry and Tuna Salad ④ POINTS VALUE

level	technique	prep	cook	serves
Basic	Simmer pg. 22	15 min	50 min	6

- ◆ 3/4 cup wheat berries
- 1 1/2 teaspoons grated lemon zest
- 1/4 cup lemon juice
- 1 tablespoon extra-virgin olive oil
- 1/2 teaspoon salt
- 1/4 teaspoon black pepper
- ◆ 1 pint cherry tomatoes, halved
- ◆ 1 (14-ounce) can quartered artichokes, drained
- ◆ 1/2 cup pitted black or green olives, coarsely chopped
- 1/2 cup lightly packed fresh mint leaves, chopped
- 2 tablespoons capers, rinsed
- ◆ 1 (12-ounce) can solid white tuna in water, drained and flaked
- ◆ 6 cups lightly packed baby arugula

1 Bring large pot of water to boil over medium-high heat; stir in wheat berries. Reduce heat and simmer, covered, until berries are tender but still chewy, 45 minutes to 1 hour. Drain.

2 Whisk together lemon zest, lemon juice, oil, salt, and pepper in large bowl. Add wheat berries, tomatoes, artichokes, olives, mint, and capers, tossing to combine. Gently stir in tuna. Let stand about 30 minutes to allow flavors to blend.

3 Divide arugula evenly among 6 plates and top evenly with salad. The salad can be refrigerated up to 4 hours. Let stand at room temperature about 30 minutes before serving.

PER SERVING (1 1/3 cups): 214 Cal, 5 g Fat, 1 g Sat Fat, 0 g Trans Fat, 15 mg Chol, 695 mg Sod, 28 g Carb, 8 g Fib, 18 g Prot, 69 mg Calc.

IN THE KITCHEN

To cut down on the cooking time of the wheat berries, put them into a bowl and add enough water to cover, then let soak for a few hours or overnight. This recipe works with the Simply Filling technique.

HOW TO... Pit an Olive

1

Place the olives on a cutting board. With the flat side of a large knife, press down firmly on each olive to crack the flesh and separate it from the pit.

2

With your fingers, remove each pit.

Tilapia with Portuguese Tomato Sauce (5 POINTS VALUE)

level	technique	prep	cook	serves
Basic	Sauté pg. 18, Simmer pg. 22	15 min	25 min	4

- 1   link fresh chorizo sausage (about 3 ounces), casing removed
- ♦ 1   medium onion, chopped
- ♦ 1   sweet banana pepper, chopped
- ♦ 1   (14½-ounce) can diced tomatoes with basil, garlic, and oregano
- ♦ 4   (¼-pound) tilapia fillets
- 1   teaspoon smoked paprika
- ¼   teaspoon salt
- ⅛   teaspoon black pepper
- 2   tablespoons chopped fresh cilantro

1 Spray medium skillet with nonstick spray and set over medium-high heat. Add sausage and cook, breaking it apart with wooden spoon, until browned, about 3 minutes. Add onion and banana pepper and cook, stirring occasionally, until vegetables are crisp-tender, about 6 minutes. Stir in tomatoes and bring to boil. Reduce heat and simmer until sauce thickens slightly, about 8 minutes.

2 Sprinkle tilapia fillets with paprika, salt, and pepper. Spray large nonstick skillet with nonstick spray and set over medium-high heat. Add tilapia and reduce heat to medium. Cook until just opaque throughout, about 3 minutes on each side. Spoon sauce evenly onto 4 plates, top each with a fillet, and sprinkle evenly with cilantro.

PER SERVING (1 tilapia fillet and about ¾ cup sauce): 234 Cal, 10 g Fat, 3 g Sat Fat, 0 g Trans Fat, 79 mg Chol, 653 mg Sod, 8 g Carb, 2 g Fib, 28 g Prot, 59 mg Calc.

IN THE KITCHEN

Sweet banana peppers are long thin peppers that range in color from pale green to yellow. They are not spicy and have a thin tender skin. You can substitute a small green bell pepper if you wish.

Chinese-Style Steamed Fish with Sugar Snap Peas (5 POINTS VALUE)

level	technique	prep	cook	serves
Basic	Steam pg. 21	10 min	10 min	4

- ◆ 4 (5-ounce) striped bass fillets, 1 inch thick
- ¼ teaspoon salt
- ◆ 2 scallions, cut into 2-inch lengths and thinly sliced lengthwise
- 1 (1½ x 1-inch) piece peeled fresh ginger, cut into matchstick-thin strips
- ◆ 4 cups sugar snap peas, trimmed
- 2 tablespoons reduced-sodium soy sauce
- 1½ teaspoons seasoned rice vinegar
- 1½ teaspoons Asian (dark) sesame oil
- Pinch red pepper flakes

1 Sprinkle bass fillets with salt and place in steamer basket; sprinkle with scallions and ginger. Set steamer basket in large skillet over 1 inch of boiling water. Cover tightly and steam 5 minutes. Place peas around fish in steamer basket. Steam until fish is just opaque throughout and peas are crisp-tender, about 2 minutes longer.

2 Meanwhile, to make sauce, stir together soy sauce, vinegar, oil, and pepper flakes in small bowl. Serve fish and peas drizzled with sauce.

PER SERVING (1 striped bass fillet, 1 cup peas, and about 2 teaspoons sauce): 217 Cal, 7 g Fat, 2 g Sat Fat, 0 g Trans Fat, 70 mg Chol, 496 mg Sod, 7 g Carb, 2 g Fib, 30 g Prot, 69 mg Calc.

◆ FILLING EXTRA

Serve the fish and peas with a bowl of brown rice (½ cup cooked brown rice per serving will increase the **POINTS** value by **2**).

CHINESE-STYLE STEAMED FISH
WITH SUGAR SNAP PEAS

Roast Cod with Fennel and Potatoes

level	technique	prep	cook	serves
Intermediate	Roast pg. 24	20 min	50 min	4

- ♦ 1¼ pounds red potatoes, sliced
- ♦ 1 large fennel bulb, halved and sliced crosswise
- ♦ 1 medium onion, halved and sliced
- 3 garlic cloves, thinly sliced
- 1½ teaspoons olive oil
- ¾ teaspoon salt
- ¼ teaspoon black pepper
- ♦ 4 (5-ounce) cod fillets
- ♦ 8 pitted brine-cured Kalamata olives, chopped
- ♦ 2 plum tomatoes, sliced
- 4 lemon wedges

1 Preheat oven to 425°F. Spray 9 x 13-inch baking dish with nonstick spray.

2 Place potatoes, fennel, onion, garlic, oil, ½ teaspoon salt, and pepper in baking dish; toss to coat. Roast, stirring twice, until potatoes are almost tender, about 30 minutes.

3 Arrange cod fillets on top of potato mixture; sprinkle with remaining ¼ teaspoon salt and olives. Arrange tomato slices in an overlapping row on top of each fillet. Roast until cod is just opaque throughout, about 20 minutes. Serve with lemon wedges.

PER SERVING (1 cod fillet and about 1 cup vegetables): 300 Cal, 5 g Fat, 1 g Sat Fat, 0 g Trans Fat, 75 mg Chol, 670 mg Sod, 35 g Carb, 7 g Fib, 30 g Prot, 101 mg Calc.

IN THE KITCHEN

Reserve the feathery tops from the fennel and chop enough to measure 1 tablespoon; sprinkle over the fish and vegetables. This recipe works with the Simply Filling technique.

Spanish Shrimp and Rice Stew

(4 POINTS VALUE)

level	technique	prep	cook	serves
Basic	Simmer pg. 22	15 min	30 min	4

2	teaspoons olive oil
♦ 1	large onion, chopped
♦ 1	celery stalk, chopped
2	garlic cloves, minced
½	cup long-grain white rice
1	teaspoon paprika
3	(8-ounce) bottles clam juice
♦ 1	(14½-ounce) can diced tomatoes
½	teaspoon dried thyme
¼	teaspoon black pepper
♦ 1	pound medium peeled and deveined shrimp
¼	cup chopped fresh flat-leaf parsley

1 Heat oil in Dutch oven over medium-high heat. Add onion, celery, and garlic; cook, stirring frequently, until softened, about 3 minutes. Add rice and paprika; cook, stirring frequently, until rice is lightly toasted, about 2 minutes.

2 Add clam juice, tomatoes, thyme, and pepper; bring to boil. Reduce heat and simmer, covered, until rice is tender, about 15 minutes.

3 Add shrimp and return to boil. Reduce heat and simmer, covered, until shrimp are just opaque in center, about 5 minutes. Stir in parsley.

PER SERVING (generous 2 cups): 227 Cal, 4 g Fat, 1 g Sat Fat, 0 g Trans Fat, 167 mg Chol, 711 mg Sod, 28 g Carb, 3 g Fib, 21 g Prot, 115 mg Calc.

♦ FILLING EXTRA

Add 1 cup frozen thawed green peas along with the shrimp in step 3.

HOW TO...
Peel and Devein Shrimp

1

To peel, starting at the head end, peel off all the shell and, if desired, the tail. To devein, use a small knife to make a cut along the center of back of the shrimp to expose the vein.

2

Use the knife to pull out the vein.

Quick Takes Shrimp

These seafood specials begin with **1 pound frozen large peeled and deveined raw shrimp.** So grab a bag and follow the directions below. Each recipe serves 4.

1 Bombay Shrimp Salad

Cook **shrimp** according to package directions; rinse under cold running water until cool. Drain well. Heat **2 teaspoons olive oil** in medium nonstick skillet over medium-high heat. Add **4 scallions, sliced,** and **1 garlic clove, finely chopped;** cook, stirring constantly, about 1 minute. Stir in **1 teaspoon curry powder** and cook just until fragrant. Transfer to serving bowl. Add **shrimp, ½ English (seedless) cucumber, sliced, ½ cup plain fat-free Greek yogurt,** and **salt and black pepper to taste;** toss to combine. This recipe works with the **Simply Filling technique.**
PER SERVING (about ³/4 cup) **POINTS** value: **3.**

2 Carribean Shrimp Salad

Cook **shrimp** according to package directions; rinse under cold running water until cool. Drain well. Whisk together **3 tablespoons lime juice, 4 teaspoons canola oil,** and **⅛ teaspoon hot pepper sauce** in serving bowl. Add shrimp, **2 cups chopped fresh pineapple, ½ jicama, peeled and diced, 2 celery stalks, sliced,** and **2 scallions, sliced;** toss to combine. This recipe works with the **Simply Filling technique.**
PER SERVING (about 1 cup) **POINTS** value: **2.**

3 Lemon-Pepper Shrimp

Heat **1 tablespoon olive oil** in large nonstick skillet over medium-high heat. Add **1 garlic clove, thinly sliced,** and cook until golden, about 1 minute. With slotted spoon, transfer to plate; set aside. Add **shrimp (thawed)** and **³/4 teaspoon lemon and pepper seasoning;** cook, stirring constantly, until just opaque in center, about 3 minutes. Stir in **1 plum tomato, chopped,** and cook until heated through, about 1 minute. Serve on **bed of arugula** and sprinkle with **reserved garlic.** This recipe works with the **Simply Filling technique.**
PER SERVING (about ³/4 cup) **POINTS** value: **3.**

4 Shrimp-Miso Soup

Whisk together **¼ cup miso** and **1 cup water** in small bowl until blended; set aside. Bring **4 cups water** to boil in large saucepan. Add **1½ cups frozen shelled edamame** and cook, covered, until tender, about 5 minutes. Stir in **1 (5- to 6-ounce) bag baby spinach,** in batches, until wilted. Add **shrimp (thawed)** and miso mixture; cook until shrimp are just opaque in center, about 1 minute. This recipe works with the **Simply Filling technique.**
PER SERVING (about 1½ cups) **POINTS** value: **4.**

5 Shrimp Puttanesca

Heat **1 tablespoon olive oil** in nonstick skillet over medium-high heat. Add **shrimp (thawed), 2 garlic cloves,** and **¼ teaspoon red pepper flakes;** cook, stirring constantly, until shrimp are just opaque in center, about 3 minutes. With slotted spoon, transfer shrimp to plate; set aside. Add **1 (14-ounce) jar marinara sauce, 6 chopped Kalamata olives** and **1 tablespoon drained capers** to skillet; bring to boil. Reduce heat and simmer about 5 minutes. Stir in shrimp and cook just until heated through, about 1 minute longer.
PER SERVING (about 1 cup) **POINTS** value: **5.**

Garlic Shrimp and Pasta with Tomatoes and Rosemary ⑦

level	technique	prep	cook	serves
Basic	Boil pg. 22, Sauté pg. 18	10 min	10 min	4

- 1 (9-ounce) package fresh spinach fettuccine or linguine
- 3 teaspoons olive oil
- ♦ 1 pound large peeled and deveined shrimp
- 4 garlic cloves, minced
- 2 teaspoons grated lemon zest
- 1½ teaspoons chopped fresh rosemary
- ½ teaspoon salt
- ¼ teaspoon black pepper
- ¼ teaspoon red pepper flakes
- ♦ 4 large plum tomatoes, chopped
- ♦ ½ cup Chicken Stock (page 32) or store-bought reduced-sodium chicken broth
- 2 tablespoons grated Parmesan cheese

1 Cook pasta according to package directions, omitting salt if desired; drain and keep warm.

2 Meanwhile, heat 2 teaspoons oil in large nonstick skillet over medium-high heat. Add shrimp and 2 cloves garlic; cook, stirring often, until shrimp are pink, but not cooked through, about 2 minutes. Transfer to plate.

3 Add remaining 1 teaspoon oil to skillet. Add remaining 2 cloves garlic, lemon zest, rosemary, salt, black pepper, and pepper flakes. Cook, stirring constantly, until fragrant, about 30 seconds. Add tomatoes and cook until softened, about 2 minutes. Add stock and boil 1 minute. Stir in shrimp and cook until just opaque in center, about 1 minute longer. Spoon pasta onto large serving platter; top with shrimp mixture and sprinkle with Parmesan.

PER SERVING (1 cup pasta, generous ¾ cup sauce, and 1½ teaspoons Parmesan): 330 Cal, 8 g Fat, 2 g Sat Fat, 0 g Trans Fat, 202 mg Chol, 806 mg Sod, 37 g Carb, 2 g Fib, 26 g Prot, 105 mg Calc.

◆FILLING EXTRA

Add a 15½-ounce can rinsed and drained canned white beans and an additional ½ cup chicken broth along with the tomatoes. The per-serving **POINTS** value will increase by **1.**

Shrimp and Spinach Salad with Lemon Dressing 3 POINTS VALUE

level	technique	prep	cook	serves
Basic	Broil pg. 25	15 min	5 min	4

- ¼ cup finely chopped fresh flat-leaf parsley
- 2 tablespoons grated lemon zest
- 1 garlic clove, minced
- 3 teaspoons extra-virgin olive oil
- ½ teaspoon salt
- ♦ 1 pound large peeled and deveined shrimp
- 2 tablespoons lemon juice
- ♦ 1 (6-ounce) container baby spinach
- ♦ ½ cucumber, peeled, seeded, and sliced
- ♦ 1 medium red bell pepper, thinly sliced

1 Spray broiler rack with nonstick spray and preheat broiler.

2 Stir together parsley, lemon zest, garlic, 1 teaspoon oil, and ¼ teaspoon salt in medium bowl; add shrimp and toss to coat.

3 Place shrimp on broiler rack and broil 5 inches from heat, turning once, until just opaque throughout, about 5 minutes.

4 Meanwhile, to make dressing, whisk together lemon juice and remaining 2 teaspoons oil and ¼ teaspoon salt in large bowl. Add spinach, cucumber, and bell pepper to dressing; toss to coat. Divide salad evenly among 4 plates. Top evenly with shrimp.

PER SERVING (about 4 shrimp and 1½ cups salad): 138 Cal, 5 g Fat, 1 g Sat Fat, 0 g Trans Fat, 161 mg Chol, 518 mg Sod, 5 g Carb, 2 g Fib, 19 g Prot, 91 mg Calc.

♦ FILLING EXTRA

Add 1 large chopped tomato to the salad. This recipe works with the Simply Filling technique.

Scallop and Asparagus Stir-Fry (4 POINTS VALUE)

level	technique	prep	cook	serves
Basic	Stir-Fry pg. 19	15 min	10 min	4

- ♦ 1   pound sea scallops
-   2   tablespoons reduced-sodium soy sauce
-   1   tablespoon minced peeled fresh ginger
- ♦ 1   pound asparagus, trimmed and cut into 2-inch lengths
-   1   orange or red bell pepper, cut into 2-inch long strips
-   2   garlic cloves, minced
-   1/8   teaspoon red pepper flakes
-   2   teaspoons canola oil
-   1   cup lightly packed fresh basil leaves, coarsely chopped
- ♦ 2   cups hot cooked brown rice

1 Toss together scallops, 1 tablespoon soy sauce, and ginger in medium bowl.

2 Spray large deep nonstick skillet with nonstick spray and set over medium-high heat until a drop of water sizzles on it. Add asparagus and bell pepper; stir-fry until crisp-tender, about 5 minutes. Stir in garlic and pepper flakes; stir-fry until fragrant, about 30 seconds. Transfer to plate.

3 Add oil to skillet. Add scallop mixture and stir-fry until scallops are browned and just opaque throughout, about 3 minutes. Add asparagus mixture and remaining 1 tablespoon soy sauce; stir-fry until heated through, about 1 minute longer. Remove skillet from heat and stir in basil. Serve over rice.

PER SERVING (generous 1 cup scallop mixture with ½ cup rice): 226 Cal, 4 g Fat, 0 g Sat Fat, 0 g Trans Fat, 30 mg Chol, 425 mg Sod, 29 g Carb, 6 g Fib, 18 g Prot, 115 mg Calc.

IN THE KITCHEN

This stir-fry would also work well with shrimp. You can substitute other vegetables for the asparagus, such as a mixture of thinly sliced onion and broccoli florets; you will need about 3 cups. This recipe works with the Simply Filling technique.

Curried Steamed Mussels with Oven Frites ⑥

level	technique	prep	cook	serves
Intermediate	Bake pg. 27, Simmer pg. 22	15 min	40 min	4

- ♦ 3   baking potatoes (about $\frac{1}{2}$ pound each), each cut lengthwise into 12 wedges
- 3   teaspoons olive oil
- $\frac{1}{2}$ teaspoon salt
- $\frac{1}{8}$ teaspoon black pepper
- 2   large shallots, finely chopped
- 3   garlic cloves, minced
- 2   teaspoons curry powder
- ♦ 1   ($14\frac{1}{2}$-ounce) can diced tomatoes
- $\frac{1}{2}$ cup water
- ♦ 2   pounds mussels, scrubbed and debearded
- $\frac{3}{4}$ cup light coconut milk
- 1   lime, cut into wedges

1 Preheat oven to 425°F. Spray large rimmed baking pan with nonstick spray.

2 Place potatoes in baking pan; drizzle with 2 teaspoons oil, sprinkle with $\frac{1}{4}$ teaspoon salt, and pepper and toss to coat. Arrange in single layer on pan with cut sides down. Bake until browned on bottom, 25 minutes. Turn potatoes onto opposite cut sides and bake until browned, 15 minutes longer.

3 Meanwhile, heat remaining 1 teaspoon oil in large deep nonstick skillet over medium heat. Add shallots and cook, stirring occasionally, until softened, about 5 minutes. Add garlic and curry powder; cook, stirring constantly, until fragrant, 30 seconds. Add tomatoes, water, and remaining $\frac{1}{4}$ teaspoon salt. Bring to boil. Reduce heat and simmer, covered, 10 minutes.

4 Increase heat to medium-high; add mussels. Cook, covered, until mussels open, about 4 minutes. Discard any mussels that do not open. With slotted spoon, divide mussels among 4 bowls. Add coconut milk to skillet; simmer 1 minute. Ladle sauce evenly over mussels. Serve with potatoes and lime wedges.

PER SERVING (about 13 mussels, $\frac{1}{2}$ cup sauce, and 9 potato wedges): 300 Cal, 7 g Fat, 2 g Sat Fat, 0 g Trans Fat, 34 mg Chol, 529 mg Sod, 43 g Carb, 5 g Fib, 19 g Prot, 121 mg Calc.

Lemon-Basil Clam Chowder

level	technique	prep	cook	serves
Basic	Sauté pg. 18, Simmer pg. 22	20 min	25 min	4

	4	teaspoons olive oil
♦	1½	cups chopped fresh fennel
♦	1	onion, chopped
♦	1	celery stalk, chopped
	3	cups water
♦	1	cup canned stewed tomatoes, coarsely chopped, with their juice
	1	cup bottled clam juice or fish broth
♦	1	all-purpose potato, peeled and chopped
	⅛	teaspoon black pepper
♦	1	(6½-ounce) can minced clams with their juice
	2	tablespoons chopped fresh basil
	½	teaspoon grated lemon zest
	2	teaspoons fresh lemon juice

1 Heat oil in large saucepan over medium-high heat. Add fennel, onion, and celery; cook, stirring occasionally, until softened, about 5 minutes.

2 Add water, tomatoes, clam juice, potato, and pepper. Cover and simmer until vegetables are tender, 15 minutes. Stir in clams with their juice, basil, lemon zest, and lemon juice. Cook until heated through (do not boil).

PER SERVING (1½ cups): 194 Cal, 6 g Fat, 1 g Sat Fat, 0 g Trans Fat, 33 mg Chol, 350 mg Sod, 22 g Carb, 3 g Fib, 14 g Prot, 103 mg Calc.

This recipe works with the Simply Filling technique.

**CLAMS STEAMED IN
CHILE BROTH WITH
ANGEL HAIR PASTA**

Clams Steamed in Chile Broth with Angel Hair Pasta (6 POINTS VALUE)

level	technique	prep	cook	serves
Intermediate	Boil pg. 22, Sauté pg. 18	15 min	20 min	4

- ◆ 6 ounces whole wheat capellini
- 2 teaspoons canola oil
- 3 garlic cloves, minced
- ◆ 3 scallions, chopped
- ◆ ½ red bell pepper, chopped
- 2 teaspoons minced peeled fresh ginger
- ¼ teaspoon red pepper flakes
- 1 cup water
- 3 tablespoons dry sherry
- 1 tablespoon reduced-sodium soy sauce
- ◆ 3 dozen littleneck clams, scrubbed
- 3 tablespoons chopped fresh cilantro

1 Cook capellini according to package directions, omitting salt if desired.

2 Meanwhile, heat oil in large deep skillet over medium heat. Add garlic and cook, stirring constantly, until fragrant, about 30 seconds. Add scallions, bell pepper, ginger, and pepper flakes and cook, stirring constantly, 1 minute. Add water, sherry, and soy sauce; bring to boil.

3 Add clams and simmer, covered, until shells open, about 8 minutes. Discard any clams that do not open.

4 Divide pasta among 4 shallow bowls; top evenly with clam mixture. Sprinkle evenly with cilantro.

PER SERVING (about 1½ cups): 323 Cal, 5 g Fat, 0 g Sat Fat, 0 g Trans Fat, 60 mg Chol, 390 mg Sod, 40 g Carb, 4 g Fib, 30 g Prot, 118 g Calc.

IN THE KITCHEN

To prevent clams from overcooking and becoming tough, use a slotted spoon to remove them from the skillet as they open. Any clams that have not opened after about 8 minutes of cooking should not be eaten.

CHAPTER 8

Beans & Grains

If you want to eat more dried beans and grains but you're not sure what dishes to make with them, these recipes are an easy introduction. Simple to prepare, full of robust flavor, and high in fiber, beans and grains are good-for-you carbs. These tasty dishes will inspire you and your family to eat more healthfully.

Turkey and Rice Arancini 8 POINTS VALUE

level	technique	prep	cook	serves
Intermediate	Sauté pg. 18, Bake pg. 27	25 min	30 min	4

- ♦ 1 (5¼-ounce) package boil-in-the-bag brown rice
- ½ pound sweet or hot Italian-style turkey sausage, casings removed
- ♦ 1 onion, finely chopped
- ♦ ½ cup fat-free mozzarella cheese, finely diced
- 3 tablespoons grated Parmesan cheese
- ♦ 3 large egg whites
- 1 tablespoon water
- ½ cup plain dried bread crumbs
- ♦ 1 cup Homemade Marinara Sauce (page 34) or tomato sauce, heated

1 Preheat oven to 425°F. Spray large baking sheet with nonstick spray.

2 Cook rice according to package directions; transfer to large bowl.

3 Spray large nonstick skillet with nonstick spray and set over medium-high heat. Add sausage and onion; cook, breaking sausage apart with wooden spoon, until sausage is no longer pink and onion is tender, about 6 minutes. Stir sausage mixture into rice. Let cool to room temperature. Stir in mozzarella, Parmesan, and 2 egg whites.

4 Whisk together remaining egg white and water in medium bowl. Place bread crumbs on sheet of wax paper. With wet hands, shape rice mixture into 8 balls, using about ⅓ cup for each. Dip balls, one at a time, into egg white mixture, then gently roll in crumbs to coat.

5 Place balls on baking sheet; lightly spray with nonstick spray. Bake, turning occasionally, until arancini are browned and heated through, about 20 minutes. Serve with marinara sauce.

PER SERVING (2 rice balls and ¼ cup sauce): 396 Cal, 11 g Fat, 3 g Sat Fat, 0 g Trans Fat, 58 mg Chol, 978 mg Sod, 48 g Carb, 4 g Fib, 28 g Prot, 271mg Calc.

♦ FILLING EXTRA

Toss together 6 cups arugula, 1 cup torn radicchio, and ¼ cup thinly sliced sweet onion with a sprinkling of lemon juice to round out the meal.

TURKEY AND RICE
ARANCINI

Quick Takes Canned Beans

Grab a can (or two) of beans from the pantry, add our quick fixings from below, and you've got a hearty meal in no time flat! Each recipe serves 4.

1 Bean and Cabbage Soup

Heat **1 tablespoon olive oil** in large saucepan over medium heat. Add **3 cups thinly sliced green cabbage, 1 large carrot, sliced, 2 garlic cloves, minced,** and **salt and black pepper** to taste. Cook, covered, until cabbage begins to wilt, about 2 minutes. Stir in **2 (14½-ounce) cans reduced-sodium chicken broth** and **1 (14 ½-ounce) can diced tomatoes, undrained.** Cook, covered, until vegetables are softened, about 8 minutes. Puree **1¼ cups beans from 2 (15½-ounce) cans Great Northern beans, rinsed and drained.** Add pureed beans and whole beans to soup and cook about 2 minutes longer. This recipe works with the **Simply Filling technique.**
PER SERVING (about 1½ cups) **POINTS** value: **5.**

2 Italian Salmon and Bean Salad

Combine **1 (15½-ounce) can cannellini (white kidney) beans, rinsed and drained, 1 (7½-ounce) can salmon, drained and flaked, 1 tomato, diced, ½ fennel bulb, trimmed and chopped, ½ small red onion, chopped, 6 chopped pitted brine-cured Kalamata olives, 2 tablespoons lemon juice, 1 tablespoon olive oil, 2 teaspoons chopped fresh rosemary,** and **black pepper** to taste in serving bowl; toss well. This recipe works with the **Simply Filling technique.**
PER SERVING (about ¾ cup) **POINTS** value: **4.**

3 Stovetop "Baked" Beans

Combine **1 (15½-ounce) can navy beans, rinsed and drained, 1 (15½-ounce) can red kidney beans, rinsed and drained, ½ cup reduced-sugar ketchup, 1 tablespoon prepared horseradish, drained, 1 teaspoon packed brown sugar,** and **1 teaspoon Worcestershire sauce** in large saucepan; bring to boil over medium-high heat. Reduce heat and simmer until flavors are blended, about 5 minutes.
PER SERVING (about ¾ cup) **POINTS** value: **5.**

4 Chickpea, Spinach, and Nectarine Salad

Whisk together **2 tablespoons lemon juice, 4 teaspoons olive oil, ½ teaspoon ground cumin, 1 garlic clove, finely chopped,** and **salt and black pepper** to taste in serving bowl. Add **1 (15½-ounce) can chickpeas, rinsed and drained, 1 (10-ounce) bag baby spinach,** and **3 nectarines, halved, pitted, and sliced;** toss well. This recipe works with the **Simply Filling technique.**
PER SERVING (about 1 cup) **POINTS** value: **4.**

5 Tex-Mex–Style Black Bean Burgers

Coarsely mash **1 (15½-ounce) can black beans, rinsed and drained,** with **2 tablespoons reduced-fat mayonnaise** in large bowl. Stir in **¼ cup chopped fresh cilantro, 1 tablespoon plain dried bread crumbs,** and **1 teaspoon chili powder.** Form into 4 patties about ½ inch thick. Spray large nonstick skillet with nonstick spray and set over medium heat. Add patties and spray with nonstick spray. Cook until heated through, about 3 minutes on each side. Serve with **½ cup fat-free salsa.**
PER SERVING (1 burger and 2 tablespoons salsa) **POINTS** value: **2.**

White Bean Stew with Crisp Pancetta and Rosemary (3 POINTS VALUE)

level	technique	prep	cook	serves
Basic	Sauté pg. 18, Simmer pg. 22	5 min	20 min	6

	2	ounces thinly sliced pancetta, cut into strips
♦	1	small onion, halved and sliced
♦	1	carrot, chopped
♦	1	celery stalk, chopped
	2	garlic cloves, minced
♦	2	(15-ounce) cans cannellini (white kidney) beans, rinsed and drained
♦	1	cup Chicken Stock (page 32) or store-bought reduced-sodium chicken broth
	2	tablespoons chopped fresh rosemary
	½	teaspoon salt
	¼	teaspoon black pepper

1 Cook pancetta in large nonstick skillet over medium-high heat until crisp; drain on paper towels.

2 Add onion, carrot, and celery to skillet and cook, stirring occasionally, until softened, 5 minutes. Add garlic and cook, stirring constantly, until fragrant, 30 seconds.

3 Add beans, stock, rosemary, salt, and pepper; bring to boil. Reduce heat and simmer, covered, until vegetables are tender, about 10 minutes. Stir in pancetta.

PER SERVING (1 cup): 167 Cal, 2 g Fat, 1 g Sat Fat, 0 g Trans Fat, 3 mg Chol, 629 mg Sod, 27 g Carb, 7 g Fib, 12 g Prot, 101 mg Calc.

♦ FILLING EXTRA

To make a heartier stew, stir in 1 large chopped peeled tomato, if desired, and 2 cups chopped fresh spinach during the last 5 minutes of cooking.

HOW TO...
Peel a Tomato

1

Bring a large saucepan of water to a boil. Cut a small, shallow cross in the bottom (blossom end) of the tomato. Lower the tomato into the water and cook 30 seconds, then plunge into a bowl of ice water.

2

With a small knife, peel away the skin. This method works for peaches too.

Greek Chicken and Pasta Salad with Tzatziki Dressing (6 POINTS VALUE)

level	technique	prep	cook	serves
Basic	Boil pg. 22, Sauté pg. 18	15 min	20 min	6

- ◆ 8 ounces whole wheat penne
- ◆ ½ cup peeled, seeded, and diced cucumber
- ½ cup fat-free mayonnaise
- ¼ cup fat-free plain yogurt
- ◆ 3 tablespoons chopped scallions
- 1 tablespoon lemon juice
- 1 teaspoon Dijon mustard
- ½ teaspoon salt
- ¼ teaspoon black pepper
- ◆ 4 (5-ounce) skinless boneless chicken breasts
- ½ teaspoon dried oregano
- 2 cups baby spinach
- ◆ 1 cup grape or cherry tomatoes, halved
- ◆ 1 red or yellow bell pepper, thinly sliced
- ◆ ¼ cup pitted brine-cured Kalamata olives, halved

1 Cook pasta according to package directions omitting salt, if desired; drain. Rinse under cold running water; drain and transfer to large bowl.

2 Meanwhile, to make dressing, puree cucumber, mayonnaise, yogurt, scallions, lemon juice, mustard, ¼ teaspoon salt, and ⅛ teaspoon pepper in blender or food processor.

3 Sprinkle chicken with oregano and remaining ¼ teaspoon salt and ⅛ teaspoon pepper. Spray large nonstick skillet with nonstick spray and set over medium-high heat. Add chicken and cook, turning occasionally, until browned and cooked through, about 8 minutes. Transfer chicken to cutting board; let stand about 5 minutes, then cut each breast into thin slices.

4 Add chicken, spinach, tomatoes, bell pepper, and olives to pasta. Add dressing and toss to coat. Serve at once.

PER SERVING (1½ cups): 329 Cal, 6 g Fat, 2 g Sat Fat, 0 g Trans Fat, 61 mg Chol, 651 mg Sod, 39 g Carb, 4 g Fib, 29 g Prot, 65 mg Calc.

IN THE KITCHEN

If you leave out the spinach, you can make the salad a day ahead. Cover and store in the refrigerator; stir in the spinach just before serving. This recipe works with the Simply Filling technique.

Sweet Chili-Glazed Chicken with Quinoa Pilaf (5 POINTS VALUE)

level	technique	prep	cook	serves
Basic	Simmer pg. 22, Sauté pg. 18	10 min	30 min	4

- ¼ cup sweet chili sauce
- 2 teaspoons grated lime zest
- 1 teaspoon lime juice
- 2 teaspoons canola oil
- ♦ 2 scallions, thinly sliced
- 1 garlic clove
- ½ teaspoon ground cumin
- ♦ 2 cups Chicken Stock (page 32) or store-bought reduced-sodium chicken broth
- 1 cup quinoa, rinsed
- 2 tablespoons dried currants
- ♦ 4 (¼-pound) chicken cutlets
- ½ teaspoon salt

1 To make glaze, combine chili sauce, lime zest, and lime juice in small bowl.

2 To make pilaf, heat oil in medium saucepan over medium-high heat. Add scallions, garlic, and cumin. Cook, stirring constantly, until fragrant, about 30 seconds. Add stock, quinoa, and currants; bring to boil. Reduce heat and simmer, covered, until quinoa is tender and liquid is absorbed, about 20 minutes. Remove from heat; keep quinoa warm.

3 Meanwhile, sprinkle chicken with salt. Spray large nonstick skillet with nonstick spray and set over medium-high heat. Add chicken and cook, turning frequently and basting with glaze, until chicken is cooked through, about 6 minutes. Serve with pilaf.

PER SERVING (1 chicken cutlet and ¾ cup pilaf): 250 Cal, 6 g Fat, 1 g Sat Fat, 0 g Trans Fat, 47 mg Chol, 516 mg Sod, 24 g Carb, 3 g Fib, 23 g Prot, 37 mg Calc.

♦FILLING EXTRA

Serve the chicken and pilaf with sliced mango (½ of a small mango, sliced per serving will increase the **POINTS** value by **1**).

Pesto Salmon Fillets over French Lentils (9 POINTS VALUE)

level	technique	prep	cook	serves
Basic	Simmer pg. 22, Pan Sear pg. 20	10 min	35 min	4

- 1   teaspoon olive oil
- ♦ 1   onion, chopped
- ♦ 1   carrot, chopped
- 2   garlic cloves, minced
- ♦ 3   cups Chicken Stock (page 32) or store-bought reduced-sodium chicken broth
- ♦ 1   cup green (French) lentils, picked over and rinsed
- 3   fresh thyme sprigs or ½ teaspoon dried thyme
- ½   teaspoon salt
- 2   tablespoons walnuts, toasted and chopped
- ♦ 4   (5-ounce) skinless salmon fillets
- ⅛   teaspoon black pepper
- 4   teaspoons Spinach-Basil Pesto Sauce (page 42) or store-bought basil pesto sauce

1 Heat oil in medium nonstick saucepan over medium-high heat. Add onion and carrot and cook, stirring occasionally, until vegetables are softened, about 5 minutes. Add garlic, and cook, stirring constantly, until fragrant, 30 seconds.

2 Add stock, lentils, thyme, and ¼ teaspoon salt; bring to boil. Reduce heat and simmer, covered, until lentils are tender and liquid is absorbed, about 25 minutes. Remove saucepan from heat; discard thyme sprigs. Stir in walnuts; keep warm.

3 Meanwhile, spray large nonstick skillet with nonstick spray and set over medium-high heat. Sprinkle salmon with remaining ¼ teaspoon salt and pepper. Place salmon in skillet and cook until just opaque in center, about 4 minutes on each side. Brush tops of fillets with pesto. Serve with lentils.

PER SERVING (1 salmon fillet, 1 teaspoon pesto, and ¾ cup lentils): 443 Cal, 14 g Fat, 3 g Sat Fat, 0 g Trans Fat, 93 mg Chol, 701 mg Sod, 34 g Carb, 9 g Fib, 47 g Prot, 78 mg Calc.

Beans, Peas & Lentils

Homecooked beans and lentils have a wonderful flavor and "meaty" texture that's far superior to the canned variety. They are inexpensive, a great source of protein, and a delicious way to boost fiber in your diet. All dried beans and lentils work with the **Simply Filling technique.** A few pointers on these healthy gems:

• Dried beans do not have to soak before cooking. Soaking saves 15-30 minutes of cooking time, but doesn't affect the taste or texture of the beans. Lentils and split peas cook in 30 minutes or less and also do not need to soak.

• Cook dried beans and lentils in water to cover them by at least 2 inches. For 1 pound of beans or lentils, add 1½ to 2 teaspoons of salt to the water at the beginning of cooking. Check often as they cook to make sure they are covered with water at all times.

• One pound of dried beans or lentils will make about 5 cups once they are cooked.

• Store cooked beans and lentils in the refrigerator up to 4 days to use in soups, stews, casseroles, salads, or dips. Or freeze them up to 6 months.

Type of bean, pea or lentil (1 pound)	Bring to a boil, then cover and simmer	*POINTS* value in ½ cup serving	Fiber in ½ cup serving
Black beans	1½ hours	*2 POINTS*	7 grams
Cannellini beans	1 hour	*2 POINTS*	5 grams
Chickpeas	2 hours	*2 POINTS*	6 grams
Red kidney beans	2 hours	*1 POINT*	7 grams
Lima beans	1 hour	*1 POINT*	7 grams
Pinto beans	1½ hours	*2 POINTS*	8 grams
Brown lentils	30 minutes	*2 POINTS*	8 grams
Green lentils	25 minutes	*2 POINTS*	5 grams
Green split peas	30 minutes	*2 POINTS*	8 grams

Moroccan Harira (5 POINTS VALUE)

level	technique	prep	cook	serves
Basic	Sauté pg. 18, Simmer pg. 22	10 min	40 min	6

- 2 teaspoons canola oil
- ♦ 1 onion, diced
- ♦ 2 celery stalks, diced
- 1 teaspoon cinnamon
- 1 teaspoon turmeric
- ¾ teaspoon black pepper
- 4 cups water
- ♦ 4 cups Vegetable Stock (page 30) or store-bought reduced-sodium vegetable broth
- ♦ 1 (15½-ounce) can chickpeas, rinsed and drained
- ♦ 1 (14½-ounce) can diced fire-roasted tomatoes
- ♦ 1 cup brown lentils, picked over and rinsed
- ¾ cup fine egg noodles
- ¼ cup chopped fresh cilantro
- 6 lemon wedges

1 Heat oil in large saucepan over medium-high heat. Add onion and celery; cook, stirring occasionally, until softened, about 5 minutes. Add cinnamon, turmeric, and pepper; cook, stirring constantly, until fragrant, 30 seconds.

2 Add water, stock, chickpeas, tomatoes, and lentils; bring to boil. Reduce heat and simmer, partially covered, until lentils are tender, about 30 minutes.

3 Stir in noodles and cook until tender, about 3 minutes. Remove from heat; stir in chopped cilantro. Serve with lemon wedges.

PER SERVING (1⅓ cups): 253 Cal, 4 g Fat, 0 g Sat Fat, 0 g Trans Fat, 4 mg Chol, 468 mg Sod, 44 g Carb, 10 g Fib, 14 g Prot, 91 mg Calc.

♦ FILLING EXTRA

A crunchy salad of watercress, tomatoes, and diced cucumbers tossed with lime juice is the perfect accompaniment for this traditional Moroccan soup.

Lentil Falafel Sandwiches

level	technique	prep	cook	serves
Basic	Simmer pg. 22, Broil pg. 25	15 min	40 min	4

- 4 cups water
- ♦ 3/4 cup brown lentils, picked over and rinsed
- ♦ 1 onion, finely chopped
- ♦ 1 carrot, finely chopped
- 3/4 teaspoon salt
- 1 tablespoon curry powder
- 1 teaspoon ground cumin
- 1/3 cup plain dried bread crumbs
- ♦ 1 large egg white
- 4 (6-inch) multigrain pitas, warmed
- ♦ 1/2 cup plain fat-free yogurt

1 To make falafel, combine water, lentils, onion, carrot, and 1/2 teaspoon salt in medium saucepan and bring to boil over medium-high heat. Reduce heat and simmer, covered, until lentils are tender, about 30 minutes. Drain and let cool.

2 Spray broiler rack with nonstick spray and preheat broiler.

3 Combine lentil mixture, curry powder, cumin, and remaining 1/4 teaspoon salt in food processor and pulse until well combined; transfer to large bowl. Add bread crumbs and egg white, stirring to mix well. With wet hands, form mixture into 12 balls and place 1 inch apart on broiler rack. Flatten balls to form 2-inch patties and spray with nonstick spray. Broil 6 inches from heat until golden brown, about 2 minutes on each side.

4 Cut a pocket in each pita. Fill each pita with 3 patties. Drizzle each sandwich with 2 tablespoons yogurt.

PER SERVING (1 sandwich): 338 Cal, 2 g Fat, 0 g Sat Fat, 0 g Trans Fat, 1 mg Chol, 699 mg Sod, 63 g Carb, 10 g Fib, 19 g Prot, 150 mg Calc.

♦ FILLING EXTRA

Add lettuce leaves, sliced cucumber, and chopped tomatoes to sandwiches.

**TWO-BEAN
MINESTRONE**

Two-Bean Minestrone (6 POINTS VALUE)

level	technique	prep	cook	serves
Basic	Sauté pg. 18, Simmer pg. 22	15 min	30 min	6

2   teaspoons olive oil

♦ 2   carrots, halved lengthwise and sliced

♦ 1   celery stalk, sliced

♦ 1   onion, diced

2   garlic cloves, minced

♦ 7   cups Vegetable Stock (page 30) or store-bought reduced-sodium vegetable broth

♦ 1   (15½-ounce) can red kidney beans, rinsed and drained

♦ 1   (15½-ounce) can chickpeas, rinsed and drained

♦ 1   cup whole wheat macaroni or other small pasta

2   teaspoons dried oregano

♦ 1   large tomato, chopped

♦ 1   small zucchini, chopped

⅓   cup chopped fresh flat-leaf parsley

6   tablespoons grated Parmesan cheese

1 Heat oil in Dutch oven over medium-high heat. Add carrots, celery, and onion and cook, stirring occasionally, until softened, 5 minutes. Add garlic and cook, stirring constantly, until fragrant, 30 seconds.

2 Add stock, kidney beans, chickpeas, macaroni, and oregano and bring to boil. Reduce heat and simmer, partially covered, 10 minutes. Stir in tomato and zucchini and simmer until pasta and vegetables are very tender, 10 minutes longer. Stir in parsley. Sprinkle each serving with 1 tablespoon Parmesan.

PER SERVING (1 bowl): 302 Cal, 5 g Fat, 2 g Sat Fat, 0 g Trans Fat, 5 mg Chol, 816 mg Sod, 51 g Carb, 10 g Fib, 16 g Prot, 172 mg Calc.

♦ FILLING EXTRA

Add one or more of the following to the soup along with the zucchini in step 2: 1 yellow squash, chopped, 2 cups chopped Swiss chard, or 1 cup frozen corn kernels.

Mushroom-Barley Stuffed Cabbage

level	technique	prep	cook	serves
Intermediate	Sauté pg. 18, Bake pg. 27	30 min	2 hr	4

♦ 1   cup pearl barley

3   cups water

♦ 8   large Savoy cabbage leaves

2   teaspoons canola oil

♦ 1   (8-ounce) package cremini mushrooms, thinly sliced

♦ 1   onion, finely chopped

1   teaspoon reduced-sodium soy sauce

3   tablespoons chopped fresh parsley

♦ 2   cups Homemade Marinara Sauce (page 34)
      or tomato sauce

1   cup water

2   teaspoons apple cider vinegar

1 Combine barley and water in medium saucepan and bring to boil over medium-high heat. Reduce heat and simmer, covered, until barley is just tender, about 30 minutes; drain.

2 Meanwhile, bring large pot of water to boil. Add cabbage leaves and return to boil. Cook until cabbage is pliable, about 8 minutes; drain. Rinse cabbage under cold running water; drain and transfer to cutting board. Trim thick ribs from base of leaves and discard.

3 Preheat oven to 350°F. Spray 9 x 13-inch baking dish with nonstick spray.

4 Heat oil in medium nonstick skillet over medium-high heat. Add mushrooms and onion; cook, stirring frequently, until softened, about 6 minutes. Add soy sauce and cook, stirring frequently, until vegetables are very tender, about 4 minutes longer. Stir in barley and parsley. Remove skillet from heat; let cool slightly.

5 Put mushroom mixture in food processor in batches and pulse until coarsely chopped. Place 1/3 cup of filling in center of each cabbage leaf. Fold in sides of each leaf over filling and roll up.

6 Spread 1/2 cup of marinara sauce on bottom of baking dish. Put rolls, seam-side down, in baking dish. Stir together remaining 1 1/2 cups marinara sauce, water, and vinegar in medium bowl; pour over rolls. Cover and bake until cabbage is very soft and sauce is bubbly, about 1 1/2 hours.

PER SERVING (2 cabbage rolls and generous 1/2 cup sauce): 282 Cal, 4 g Fat, 0 g Sat Fat, 0 g Trans Fat, 0 mg Chol, 474 mg Sod, 56 g Carb, 12 g Fib, 10 g Prot, 112 mg Calc.

This recipe works with the Simply Filling technique.

Middle Eastern Vegetarian Chili (5 POINTS VALUE)

level	technique	prep	cook	serves
Basic	Simmer pg. 22, Sauté pg. 18	15 min	50 min	6

- ♦ 1   cup wheat berries
- 1   tablespoon canola oil
- ♦ 1   onion, chopped
- ♦ 1   carrot, chopped
- 2   garlic cloves, minced
- ♦ 1   (15½-ounce) can chickpeas, rinsed and drained
- ♦ 1   (14½-ounce) can diced tomatoes
- ♦ 4   cups Vegetable Stock (page 30) or store-bought reduced-sodium vegetable broth
- 2   tablespoons harissa
- 1   tablespoon curry powder
- 1   tablespoon ground cumin
- 2   teaspoons honey

1 Bring large pot of water to boil over medium-high heat; stir in wheat berries. Reduce heat and simmer, covered, until berries are tender but still chewy, 45 minutes–1 hour. Drain.

2 Meanwhile, heat oil in large saucepan over medium-high heat. Add onion, carrot, and garlic; cook, stirring occasionally, until onion is softened, about 6 minutes. Add remaining ingredients and bring to boil. Reduce heat and simmer, covered, until vegetables are very tender, about 20 minutes. Stir in wheat berries and cook until heated through, about 3 minutes.

PER SERVING (1⅓ cups): 257 Cal, 5 g Fat, 1 g Sat Fat, 0 g Trans Fat, 0 mg Chol, 572 mg Sod, 47 g Carb, 8 g Fib, 9 g Prot, 90 mg Calc.

IN THE KITCHEN

Harissa is a spicy North African condiment made from chiles, garlic, cumin, coriander, and caraway seeds. Look for it in small jars in the ethnic foods section of large supermarkets.

Thai Shrimp with Edamame

level	technique	prep	cook	serves
Basic	Stir-Fry pg. 19	10 min	10 min	4

- ½   cup light coconut milk
- ♦ ¼   cup Chicken Stock (page 32) or store-bought reduced-sodium chicken broth
- 2   teaspoons packed light brown sugar
- 1   teaspoon Thai red curry paste
- 1   teaspoon fish sauce
- 2   teaspoons canola oil
- ♦ 1   pound large peeled and deveined shrimp
- 1   shallot, thinly sliced
- 2   garlic cloves, minced
- ♦ 1   jalapeño pepper, seeded and minced
- ♦ 1   (10-ounce) bag frozen shelled edamame (green soybeans), thawed
- ♦ 1   yellow bell pepper, cut into 1-inch pieces
- ♦ 1   red bell pepper, cut into 1-inch pieces

1 Whisk together coconut milk, stock, brown sugar, curry paste, and fish sauce in small bowl.

2 Heat large deep nonstick skillet or wok over high heat until a drop of water sizzles on it. Pour in 1 teaspoon oil and swirl to coat pan. Add shrimp and stir-fry until opaque in center, about 4 minutes. Transfer shrimp to plate.

3 Reduce heat to medium and add remaining 1 teaspoon oil to skillet. Add shallot, garlic, and jalapeño; cook, stirring constantly, until fragrant, about 30 seconds. Add edamame and bell peppers; stir-fry until bell peppers are crisp-tender, about 3 minutes.

4 Return shrimp to skillet along with coconut milk mixture. Stir-fry until liquid is thickened slightly and shrimp are heated through, about 2 minutes.

PER SERVING (1½ cups): 249 Cal, 9 g Fat, 2 g Sat Fat, 0 g Trans Fat, 161 mg Chol, 368 mg Sod, 16 g Carb, 5 g Fib, 27 g Prot, 93 mg Calc.

♦ FILLING EXTRA

Serve the stir-fry with brown basmati rice (½ cup cooked brown basmati rice for each serving will increase the **POINTS** value by **2**).

Whole Grains

Whole grains like barley, bulgur, quinoa, all types of brown rice, wild rice, and wheat berries are simple to make, and most of them don't take as long to cook as you might think. Each type has a unique flavor and texture, but all grains are nutritious, versatile, and delicious. Some helpful facts:

• Grains will add flavor and texture to your meals, as well as a good amount of fiber and trace vitamins and minerals. You can find most grains in any well-stocked supermarket, or buy them in bulk (and probably at a lower price) at a natural foods store.

• Since whole grains contain the germ of the grain, they tend to spoil quicker than processed grains (such as white rice). Store them in an airtight container in a cool, dry place up to 6 months. For longer storage, place them in the refrigerator. Store cooked grains in the refrigerator up to 4 days to use in salads, pilafs, casseroles, or soups.

• Consume a variety of grains, beans, fruits, and vegetables to fulfill the 25 to 30 grams of fiber that you need each day. All whole grains work with the **Simply Filling technique.**

Grain (1 cup)	Water	Bring to a boil, then cover and simmer	Makes	*POINTS* value in ½ cup cooked serving	Fiber in ½ cup cooked serving
Barley	3 cups	30 minutes	3½ cups	*1.5 POINTS*	3 grams
Bulgur	3 cups	12-15 minutes	3 cups	*0.5 POINTS*	4 grams
Quinoa	2 cups	20 minutes	3 cups	*2 POINTS*	2 grams
Brown rice	2 cups	40 minutes	3 cups	*2 POINTS*	2 grams
Brown basmati rice	2 cups	35 minutes	3 cups	*2 POINTS*	1 gram
Wild rice	2 cups	45 minutes	3½ cups	*1.5 POINTS*	1 gram
Wheat berries	3 cups	45-60 minutes	2 cups	*3 POINTS*	5 grams

Spaghetti with Fresh Tonato-Basil Pesto (6 POINTS VALUE)

level	technique	prep	cook	serves
Basic	Boil pg. 22	10 min	20 min	4

- ♦ 2 cups grape tomatoes
- ½ cup lightly packed fresh basil leaves
- ♦ ¼ cup sun-dried tomatoes (not oil-packed)
- 3 garlic cloves, halved
- 2 tablespoons pine nuts, toasted
- 6 tablespoons grated Parmesan cheese
- 2 teaspoons extra-virgin olive oil
- ½ teaspoon salt
- ½ teaspoon red pepper flakes
- ♦ ½ pound whole wheat thin spaghetti

1 To make pesto, combine grape tomatoes, basil, sun-dried tomatoes, garlic, pine nuts, 2 tablespoons Parmesan, oil, salt, and pepper flakes in blender or food processor; blend until smooth.

2 Meanwhile, cook spaghetti according to package directions, omitting salt if desired. Drain, reserving 2 tablespoons cooking water. Transfer spaghetti and reserved cooking water to large bowl. Add pesto; toss to coat. Sprinkle each serving with 1 tablespoon remaining Parmesan.

PER SERVING (1¼ cups pasta and sauce with 1 tablespoon Parmesan): 324 Cal, 9 g Fat, 2 g Sat Fat, 0 g Trans Fat, 7 mg Chol, 752 mg Sod, 51 g Carb, 6 g Fib, 15 g Prot, 177 mg Calc.

♦ FILLING EXTRA

Add 2 thinly sliced zucchini or yellow squash to the spaghetti during the last 3 minutes of cooking.

Ricotta Gnocchi with Sage Beurre Blanc (4 POINTS VALUE)

level	technique	prep	cook	serves
Advanced	Boil pg. 22	25 min	15 min	6

- 1 (15-ounce) container part-skim ricotta cheese
- ½ cup whole wheat flour
- 3 tablespoons grated Parmesan cheese
- ½ teaspoon salt
- 2 teaspoons olive oil
- 2 teaspoons butter
- 6 small sage leaves
- ¼ cup dry white wine
- ♦ ¼ cup Chicken Stock (page 32) or store-bought reduced-sodium chicken broth
- 1 tablespoon chopped fresh parsley

1 Stir together ricotta, flour, 2 tablespoons Parmesan, and salt in large bowl (the dough will be sticky).

2 Scrape dough onto lightly floured surface; divide into 4 pieces. Roll one piece into ½-inch-wide log. Cut into 1-inch pieces. Place gnocchi on lightly floured baking sheet and cover with damp paper towels. Repeat with remaining dough.

3 Cook oil, butter, and sage in large nonstick skillet over medium heat, stirring frequently, until sage is fragrant, about 2 minutes. Add wine and stock; bring to boil. Reduce heat and simmer until sauce just begins to thicken, about 2 minutes.

4 Meanwhile, bring large pot of water to boil. Add gnocchi, in batches, dropping them in a few at a time to prevent sticking. Simmer until gnocchi just float to surface, about 2 minutes. With slotted spoon, transfer gnocchi to sauce in skillet. Cook, stirring often, until gnocchi absorb most of sauce, about 2 minutes. Sprinkle with parsley and remaining 1 tablespoon Parmesan.

PER SERVING (about ½ cup): 175 Cal, 10 g Fat, 5 g Sat Fat, 0 g Trans Fat, 28 mg Chol, 367 mg Sod, 11 g Carb, 1 g Fib, 11 g Prot, 241 mg Calc.

♦ FILLING EXTRA

For a colorful side dish, steam a mixture of thinly sliced cabbage and carrots; toss with a drizzle of white-wine vinegar and salt and pepper to taste.

**WHITE BEAN RAVIOLI
WITH SPINACH**

White Bean Ravioli with Spinach (5 POINTS VALUE)

level	technique	prep	cook	serves
Advanced	Sauté pg. 18, Simmer pg. 22	30 min	20 min	4

- ♦ 1 cup cannellini (white kidney) beans, rinsed and drained
- 3 tablespoons grated Parmesan cheese
- 3 tablespoons part-skim ricotta cheese
- 1 tablespoon chopped fresh flat-leaf parsley
- 1 teaspoon grated lemon zest
- ¼ teaspoon salt
- 32 (3-inch) square or round wonton wrappers
- 2 teaspoons olive oil
- 3 garlic cloves, thinly sliced
- ♦ 1 bunch spinach (1¼ pounds), coarsely chopped
- ⅛ teaspoon red pepper flakes
- ♦ 3 cups Vegetable Stock (page 30) or store-bought reduced-sodium vegetable broth

1 To make filling, put beans in food processor and pulse until smooth. Add 2 tablespoons Parmesan, ricotta, parsley, lemon zest, and salt; process until smooth and creamy. Transfer to small bowl.

2 Lay 8 wonton wrappers out on work surface. (Cover remaining wontons with damp paper towels to prevent them from drying out.) Place 1 level tablespoon filling in center of each wonton wrapper. Brush edges of wontons with water. Top each filled wonton with another wonton, pressing edges to make tight seal. Place ravioli on baking sheet in one layer and cover with damp paper towels. Repeat with remaining filling and wonton wrappers to make a total of 16 ravioli.

3 Heat oil in large nonstick skillet over medium heat. Add garlic and cook until golden, about 2 minutes. Add spinach and pepper flakes and cook, stirring occasionally, until just tender, about 6 minutes. Add stock and bring to boil. Reduce heat and simmer, covered, until spinach is wilted, about 2 minutes longer.

4 Meanwhile, bring large pot of water to boil. Carefully drop ravioli into water and cook until they just begin to float, about 2 minutes; drain. Divide ravioli evenly among 4 shallow soup bowls and ladle stock mixture evenly on top. Sprinkle evenly with remaining 1 tablespoon Parmesan.

PER SERVING (1 bowl): 286 Cal, 5 g Fat, 2 g Sat Fat, 0 g Trans Fat, 11 mg Chol, 753 mg Sod, 47 g Carb, 8 g Fib, 13 g Prot, 214 mg Calc.

CHAPTER 9

Side Dishes

Whatever the season, there is a dazzling bounty of delectable, nutritious, low-calorie vegetables ready to be served alongside your favorite main dishes. Spring asparagus, summer tomatoes, fall squash, and winter root vegetables offer fresh flavors your whole family will enjoy year-round.

Steamed Asparagus with Tarragon Gremolata ⓪

level	technique	prep	cook	serves
Basic	Steam pg. 21	5 min	10 min	4

- ♦ 1   pound asparagus, trimmed
-   2   tablespoons chopped fresh tarragon
-   1½ teaspoons grated lemon zest
-   1   garlic clove, minced
-   2   teaspoons olive oil
-   ½   teaspoon salt
-   ⅛   teaspoon black pepper

1 Bring 1 inch of water to boil in large saucepan over medium-high heat. Put asparagus in steamer basket and place basket in saucepan. Cover and cook until asparagus is crisp-tender, about 5 minutes.

2 Meanwhile, to make gremolata, stir together tarragon, lemon zest, and garlic in small bowl.

3 Place asparagus on serving platter; add oil, salt, and pepper; toss to coat. Sprinkle with gremolata.

PER SERVING (¼ of asparagus): 35 Cal, 2 g Fat, 0 g Sat Fat, 0 g Trans Fat, 0 mg Chol, 296 mg Sod, 3 g Carb, 2 g Fib, 1 g Prot, 22 mg Calc.

IN THE KITCHEN

To quickly trim asparagus, bend each spear a couple of inches from the bottom and the tough end will snap off naturally. This recipe works with the Simply Filling technique.

Roasted Tomatoes with Rosemary and Balsamic Vinegar ①POINTS VALUE

level	technique	prep	cook	serves
Basic	Roast pg. 24	10 min	35 min	6

- ◆ 6 plum tomatoes (about 1¼ pounds), halved lengthwise
- 2 teaspoons olive oil
- ½ teaspoon salt
- ⅛ teaspoon black pepper
- 2 teaspoons dried rosemary, crumbled
- 2 teaspoons balsamic vinegar

1 Preheat oven to 375°F. Spray shallow baking pan with nonstick spray.

2 Combine tomatoes, oil, salt, and pepper in large bowl and toss to coat. Arrange tomatoes, cut-side up, in pan; sprinkle with rosemary. Roast until tomatoes are tender and skins wrinkle, 35–40 minutes. Transfer to serving platter and drizzle tomatoes with vinegar.

PER SERVING (2 tomato halves): 27 Cal, 2 g Fat, 0 g Sat Fat, 0 g Trans Fat, 0 mg Chol, 200 mg Sod, 3 g Carb, 1 g Fib, 1 g Prot, 9 mg Calc.

IN THE KITCHEN

Avoid using an aluminum pan for cooking any dish that contains tomatoes. The metal can have a reaction with the acid in the tomatoes, causing the finished dish to have a bitter taste. This recipe works with the Simply Filling technique.

Smoky Red Peppers with Capers ①POINTS VALUE

level	technique	prep	cook	serves
Intermediate	Broil pg. 25	15 min	15 min	4

- ◆ 4 large red or yellow bell peppers or combination
- 2 tablespoons chopped fresh flat-leaf parsley
- 1 tablespoon red-wine vinegar
- 2 tablespoons capers, drained and rinsed
- 2 teaspoons olive oil
- 2 garlic cloves, minced
- ½ teaspoon smoked or regular paprika
- ¼ teaspoon salt

1 Preheat broiler; place peppers on baking sheet and broil 5 inches from heat, turning occasionally, until blackened on all sides, 12–15 minutes. Transfer peppers to a paper bag and fold closed; let steam 10 minutes.

2 When cool enough to handle, peel peppers and cut into thick slices; transfer to medium bowl. Add parsley, vinegar, capers, oil, garlic, paprika, and salt and toss to combine. Let stand at least 15 minutes or up to 1 hour to allow flavors to develop.

PER SERVING (about ¾ cup): 69 Cal, 3 g Fat, 0 g Sat Fat, 0 g Trans Fat, 0 mg Chol, 281 mg Sod, 11 g Carb, 4 g Fib, 2g Prot, 19 mg Calc.

IN THE KITCHEN

Make a double batch of these peppers and use them to add color and flavor to sandwiches, salads, or pasta dishes. You can store them in an airtight container in the refrigerator up to 3 days. This recipe works with the Simply Filling technique.

**SMOKY RED PEPPERS
WITH CAPERS AND PORK
PARMESAN, PAGE 122**

Swiss Chard with Garlic and Grape Tomatoes (1 POINTS VALUE)

level	technique	prep	cook	serves
Basic	Sauté pg. 18	15 min	15 min	6

- 1   tablespoon olive oil
- 2   garlic cloves, thinly sliced
- ♦ ½   cup Vegetable Stock (page 30) or store-bought reduced-sodium vegetable broth
- ♦ 2   pounds Swiss chard, tough stems removed and leaves coarsely chopped
- ♦ 2   cups grape tomatoes
- ½   teaspoon salt
- ⅛   teaspoon red pepper flakes

1 Heat oil in large nonstick skillet over medium-high heat. Add garlic and cook, stirring often, until garlic is golden, about 2 minutes.

2 Add stock, then add chard, in batches if necessary, and cook, stirring often, until chard is tender and almost all liquid is evaporated, about 8 minutes. Add tomatoes, salt, and pepper flakes and cook, stirring often, until tomatoes are just softened, about 3 minutes.

PER SERVING (⅔ cup): 60 Cal, 3 g Fat, 0 g Sat Fat, 0 g Trans Fat, 0 mg Chol, 531 mg Sod, 8 g Carb, 3 g Fib, 3 g Prot, 79 mg Calc.

IN THE KITCHEN

You can use the stems of the chard in this recipe. Cut them into thin slices and add with the stock in step 2. Cook the stems until they are softened, about 3 minutes before adding the chard leaves. This recipe works with the Simply Filling technique.

Spinach with Grapes and Pine Nuts (1 POINTS VALUE)

level	technique	prep	cook	serves
Basic	Sauté pg. 18	10 min	10 min	4

- 1 teaspoon olive oil
- ♦ 1 red onion, thinly sliced
- 2 garlic cloves, minced
- 1 tablespoon water
- ♦ 2 (10-ounce) bags fresh spinach
- ¼ teaspoon salt
- ¼ teaspoon black pepper
- ♦ 1 cup seedless red grapes
- 1 tablespoon pine nuts, toasted
- 2 teaspoons red-wine vinegar

1 Heat oil in large nonstick skillet over medium-high heat. Add onion and cook, stirring occasionally, until onion is softened, about 5 minutes. Add garlic and cook, stirring frequently, until fragrant, about 30 seconds.

2 Increase heat to high. Add water, then add spinach, in batches, salt, and pepper, stirring just until each batch wilts. Add grapes and cook, stirring occasionally, until just heated through, about 2 minutes. Stir in pine nuts and red-wine vinegar.

PER SERVING (1 cup): 97 Cal, 3 g Fat, 0 g Sat Fat, 0 g Trans Fat, 0 mg Chol, 262 mg Sod, 15 g Carb, 4 g Fib, 5 g Prot, 154 mg Calc.

IN THE KITCHEN

Instead of the grapes, you can use a cup of grape tomatoes in this recipe.

Fresh Produce 101

When buying and storing fresh fruits and veggies, make sure to keep the following in mind:

Find the Freshest To get the freshest fruits and veggies, buy from local farmers markets during the growing season. In the winter months or as supplement to local produce, shop at a market that does a brisk business with quick turnover in the produce department. If you spot wilted greens and wrinkled fruit, shop elsewhere.

Buy What's Best Except for leafy greens, most fruits and vegetables should feel heavy for their size. Freshly picked produce is plump and filled with water, but as it loses freshness, water evaporates, causing the produce to shrivel and weigh less. Look for produce with smooth firm skin with no blemishes, bruises, or soft spots. Greens should have crisp glossy leaves with no signs of wilting or yellowing.

In the Fridge Most vegetables are best stored in an unsealed plastic bag in the refrigerator. Wrap greens and lettuces in paper towels and store in a sealed zip-close plastic bag in the refrigerator.

The Exceptions Always store tomatoes at room temperature to prevent them from developing a mealy texture. Allow apricots, plums, peaches, nectarines, and pears to ripen at room temperature until soft to the touch, then eat or refrigerate for up to 3 days. Finally, keep potatoes, sweet potatoes, winter squash, onions, and garlic, in a cool dark storage place.

POTATO-LEEK MASH
AND LAMB CHOPS WITH
ARTICHOKES, GARLIC,
AND MINT, PAGE 129

Potato-Leek Mash (3 POINTS VALUE)

level	technique	prep	cook	serves
Basic	Simmer pg. 22	10 min	30 min	4

2   teaspoons olive oil

♦ 2   large leeks, cleaned, pale green
   part thinly sliced

♦ 2   cups Chicken Stock (page 32) or store-bought
   reduced-sodium chicken broth

♦ 1   pound red and yellow Yukon Gold baby potatoes, halved

3   garlic cloves, chopped

♦ 3   tablespoons fat-free milk

   Pinch nutmeg

1 Heat oil in large nonstick saucepan over medium-high heat. Add leeks and ¼ cup stock. Simmer, stirring occasionally, until leeks are softened and liquid has evaporated, about 6 minutes.

2 Add potatoes, garlic, and remaining 1³⁄4 cups stock; bring to boil. Reduce heat and simmer, partially covered, until potatoes are fork-tender and most of liquid is absorbed, about 20 minutes. Remove saucepan from heat; stir in milk and nutmeg. Coarsely mash potatoes.

PER SERVING (¾ cup): 159 Cal, 3 g Fat, 1 g Sat Fat, 0 g Trans Fat, 0 mg Chol, 204 mg Sod, 29 g Carb, 4 g Fib, 5 g Prot, 73 mg Calc.

IN THE KITCHEN

Be sure to clean the leeks well as they can be quite sandy. To do this, trim away most of the dark green tops. Cut the leeks in half lengthwise and then slice them. Plunge the leeks into a bowl of cold water and lift them into a colander. Repeat, using fresh water, until no sand remains in the bottom of the bowl. This recipe works with the Simply Filling technique.

Spicy Soy-Glazed Sweet Potatoes

level	technique	prep	cook	serves
Basic	Roast pg. 24	5 min	30 min	4

- ♦ 4   medium sweet potatoes, peeled
- 2   teaspoons canola oil
- 1   tablespoon chili-garlic paste
- 1   tablespoon reduced-sodium soy sauce
- 1   tablespoon honey
- 1   lime, cut into wedges

1 Preheat oven to 400ºF. Line large rimmed baking sheet with foil; spray with nonstick spray.

2 Halve potatoes lengthwise and cut each piece lengthwise into thirds. Place on baking sheet; drizzle with oil and toss to coat. Arrange in single layer on pan with cut sides down. Roast until browned on bottom, 12–15 minutes. Turn potatoes onto opposite cut sides and roast until browned, 10 minutes longer.

3 To make glaze, stir together chili-garlic paste, soy sauce, and honey in small bowl. Brush potatoes with glaze and roast, turning and basting, until potatoes are tender, 6–8 minutes longer. Serve with lime wedges.

PER SERVING (6 wedges): 154 Cal, 3 g Fat, 0 g Sat Fat, 0 g Trans Fat, 0 mg Chol, 191 mg Sod, 31 g Carb, 5 g Fib, 3 g Prot, 55 mg Calc.

IN THE KITCHEN

If you don't like spicy dishes, omit the chili-garlic paste in the glaze.

Salad-Stuffed Mushrooms (1 POINTS VALUE)

level	technique	prep	cook	serves
Basic	Roast pg. 24	15 min	20 min	6

♦ 6   medium portobello mushrooms, stems removed

   6   tablespoons Red Wine-Shallot Vinaigrette (page 37) or reduced-fat vinaigrette salad dressing

♦ 2   cups mixed baby greens

♦ 1   medium tomato, chopped

♦ ½   cucumber, peeled, seeded, and chopped

♦ ½   red bell pepper, chopped

♦ 2   tablespoons chopped red onion

  ¼   cup crumbled reduced-fat feta cheese

1 Preheat oven to 400°F. Spray large rimmed baking pan with nonstick spray.

2 Place mushrooms in pan; brush with 3 tablespoons salad dressing. Roast, turning once, until mushrooms are tender, about 20 minutes. Let cool slightly.

3 Toss together greens, tomato, cucumber, bell pepper, onion, and remaining 3 tablespoons salad dressing in large bowl. Place a mushroom, rounded-side down, on each of 6 plates. Fill evenly with salad and sprinkle with crumbled feta.

PER SERVING (1 stuffed mushroom): 74 Cal, 3 g Fat, 1 g Sat Fat, 0 g Trans Fat, 2 mg Chol, 145 mg Sod, 9 g Carb, 2 g Fib, 4 g Prot, 47 mg Calc.

IN THE KITCHEN

To make more room for the stuffing, remove the gills from the underside of the mushrooms before roasting. To do so, simply scrape them away using a small spoon.

Roasted Eggplant–Tomato Stacks

level	technique	prep	cook	serves
Intermediate	Roast pg. 24	10 min	20 min	4

- 1 large eggplant
- ¼ teaspoon salt
- ⅛ teaspoon black pepper
- 4 tablespoons Red Wine-Shallot Vinaigrette (page 37) or reduced-fat vinaigrette salad dressing
- 1 large tomato, ends trimmed, cut into 8 slices
- 12 large fresh basil leaves
- 8 tablespoons shredded part-skim mozzarella cheese

1 Preheat oven to 400°F. Spray large rimmed baking sheet with nonstick spray.

2 Trim both ends off eggplant and cut into 12 rounds. Arrange eggplant on baking sheet in one layer and spray lightly with nonstick spray; sprinkle with salt and pepper. Roast, turning once, until lightly browned, about 20 minutes. Let cool slightly.

3 To assemble stacks, place 4 of largest eggplant slices on platter. Drizzle evenly with 1 tablespoon dressing; top each with 1 slice of tomato and 1 basil leaf. Sprinkle each with 1 tablespoon mozzarella. Repeat layering once. Top each stack with 1 slice of eggplant, drizzle evenly with remaining 2 tablespoons dressing and top with remaining basil leaves.

PER SERVING (1 eggplant stack): 140 Cal, 6 g Fat, 2 g Sat Fat, 0 g Trans Fat, 8 mg Chol, 287 mg Sod, 18 g Carb, 5 g Fib, 6 g Prot, 123 mg Calc.

◆ FILLING EXTRA

Serve each eggplant stack on a bed of mixed baby greens.

ROASTED EGGPLANT-TOMATO STACKS

White Beans and Greens

level	technique	prep	cook	serves
Basic	Sauté pg. 18, Simmer pg. 22	10 min	15 min	4

	2	teaspoons olive oil
♦	1	onion, thinly sliced
♦	1	tomato, chopped
	2	garlic cloves, minced
♦	6	cups trimmed and chopped kale
♦	1	(15½-ounce) can cannellini (white kidney) beans, rinsed and drained
♦	½	cup Chicken Stock (page 32) or store-bought reduced-sodium chicken broth
	¼	teaspoon salt
	⅛	teaspoon black pepper

1 Heat oil in large nonstick skillet over medium-high heat. Add onion and cook, stirring occasionally, until softened, about 5 minutes. Add tomato and garlic; cook, stirring occasionally, until tomato is softened, about 3 minutes.

2 Add kale, beans, stock, salt, and pepper; bring to boil. Reduce heat and simmer, partially covered, until flavors are blended and kale is tender, about 5 minutes longer.

PER SERVING (¾ cup): 198 Cal, 3 g Fat, 1 g Sat Fat, 0 g Trans Fat, 0 mg Chol, 469 mg Sod, 33 g Carb, 8 g Fib, 12 g Prot, 217 mg Calc.

IN THE KITCHEN

To make this a heartier dish, cook 4 (1-ounce) slices of diced Canadian bacon with the onion in step 1 (this will increase the per-serving **POINTS** value by **1**). This recipe works with the Simply Filling technique.

Indian Lentil and Rice Pilaf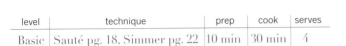

level	technique	prep	cook	serves
Basic	Sauté pg. 18, Simmer pg. 22	10 min	30 min	4

   2   teaspoons canola oil

♦ 1   large onion, thinly sliced

   2   teaspoons grated peeled fresh ginger

   2   garlic cloves, minced

♦ 3   cups Vegetable Stock (page 30) or store-bought reduced-sodium vegetable broth

  ½   cup white basmati rice

♦ ½   cup red lentils

   2   teaspoons garam masala

   1   teaspoon ground cumin

   2   tablespoons chopped fresh cilantro

1 Heat oil in medium saucepan over medium heat. Add onion and cook, stirring occasionally, until onion is tender, about 8 minutes. Add ginger and garlic and cook, stirring constantly, until fragrant, 30 seconds.

2 Transfer half of onion mixture to small bowl. Add stock, rice, lentils, garam masala, and cumin to onion mixture in saucepan. Bring to boil. Reduce heat and simmer, covered, until liquid is absorbed and rice and lentils are tender, about 20 minutes. Serve topped with reserved onion mixture.

PER SERVING (¾ cup): 212 Cal, 3 g Fat, 0 g Sat Fat, 0 g Trans Fat, 0 mg Chol, 319 mg Sod, 40 g Carb, 6 g Fib, 8 g Prot, 43 mg Calc.

◆ FILLING EXTRA

For a little tang, top each serving of this tasty pilaf with 1 tablespoon of plain fat-free Greek yogurt.

Bulgur Pilaf with Dates and Apricots ④ POINTS VALUE

level	technique	prep	cook	serves
Basic	Sauté pg. 18, Simmer pg. 22	10 min	25 min	4

- 2 teaspoons canola oil
- ♦ 1 onion, finely chopped
- 3 cups water
- ♦ 1 cup bulgur
- ½ teaspoon salt
- ½ teaspoon cinnamon
- ½ teaspoon ground cardamom
- ¼ teaspoon ground allspice
- 6 pitted dates, coarsely chopped
- 6 dried apricots, coarsely chopped
- 2 tablespoons sliced almonds, toasted
- Grated zest of 1 lemon

1 Heat oil in medium nonstick saucepan over medium-high heat. Add onion and cook, stirring occasionally, until softened, about 5 minutes.

2 Add water, bulgur, salt, cinnamon, cardamom, and allspice; bring to boil. Reduce heat and simmer, covered, until liquid is absorbed and bulgur is tender, about 15 minutes. Remove saucepan from heat; stir in dates, apricots, almonds, and lemon zest.

PER SERVING (¾ cup): 225 Cal, 4 g Fat, 0 g Sat Fat, 0 g Trans Fat, 0 mg Chol, 315 mg Sod, 45 g Carb, 9 g Fib, 6 g Prot, 51 mg Calc.

IN THE KITCHEN

To make chopping the dried fruits a breeze, use kitchen scissors lightly sprayed with nonstick spray.

Quinoa with Squash and Cranberries ③ POINTS VALUE

level	technique	prep	cook	serves
Basic	Sauté pg. 18, Simmer pg. 22	15 min	20 min	6

- 1 tablespoon canola oil
- ◆ 1 onion, diced
- ◆ 2 celery stalks, diced
- ◆ 2 cups Vegetable Stock (page 30) or store-bought reduced-sodium vegetable broth
- ◆ 2 cups peeled and diced butternut squash
- ◆ 1 cup quinoa, rinsed
- ¼ cup dried cranberries
- 2 tablespoons chopped walnuts, toasted

1 Heat oil in large saucepan over medium-high heat. Add onion and celery and cook, stirring occasionally, until softened, about 5 minutes.

2 Add stock, squash, quinoa, and cranberries; bring to boil. Reduce heat and simmer, covered, until liquid is absorbed and squash and quinoa are tender, about 15 minutes. Sprinkle with walnuts.

PER SERVING (⅔ cup): 183 Cal, 5 g Fat, 1 g Sat Fat, 0 g Trans Fat, 0 mg Chol, 154 mg Sod, 30 g Carb, 4 g Fib, 5 g Prot, 44 mg Calc.

IN THE KITCHEN

To save time, look for ready-cut and peeled butternut squash found in the produce section of many supermarkets.

HOW TO...
Prepare Butternut Squash

1

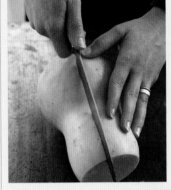

With a heavy knife, slice off the stem. Cut the squash in half lengthwise.

2

With a large spoon or ice-cream scoop, scrape out the seeds and membranes. Cut each piece of squash in half crosswise. Peel the squash and cut or slice as directed in the recipe.

Basmati Rice with Green Beans and Shallots

2 POINTS VALUE

level	technique	prep	cook	serves
Basic	Simmer pg. 22, Sauté pg. 18	15 min	40 min	4

- ♦ 2 cups Vegetable Stock (page 30) or store-bought reduced-sodium vegetable broth
- ♦ ½ cup brown basmati rice
- ♦ ½ pound green beans, trimmed and cut into 1½-inch pieces
- 2 teaspoons olive oil
- 2 shallots, thinly sliced
- ¼ cup chopped fresh flat-leaf parsley
- 2 teaspoons grated lemon zest
- ⅛ teaspoon black pepper

1 Combine stock and rice in medium saucepan; bring to boil. Reduce heat and simmer, covered, until rice is tender and liquid is absorbed, about 35 minutes.

2 Meanwhile, bring medium saucepan of water to boil. Add beans and cook just until crisp-tender, about 3 minutes. Drain.

3 Heat oil in small nonstick skillet over medium-high heat. Add shallots and cook, stirring occasionally, until lightly browned and crisp, about 2 minutes. With slotted spoon, transfer shallots to paper towels to drain. Stir green beans, parsley, lemon zest, and pepper into rice and sprinkle with shallots.

PER SERVING (½ cup): 133 Cal, 3 g Fat, 0 g Sat Fat, 0 g Trans Fat, 0 mg Chol, 217 mg Sod, 25 g Carb, 3 g Fib, 4 g Prot, 36 mg Calc.

♦ FILLING EXTRA

Add 1 cup halved cherry tomatoes to the rice along with the beans in step 3. This recipe works with the Simply Filling technique.

HOW TO...
Grate Citrus Zest

1

Scrub lemons, limes, or oranges to remove any wax coating. Hold one end of a rasp grater (preferably with a molded rubber handle for easy gripping) over a sheet of wax paper. Stroke the fruit, in one downward motion, across the grater's raised teeth so that just the colored zest is removed. Rotating the lemon, continue to grate the zest.

2

Remove any remaining zest from the grater with a small rubber spatula.

Penne and Broccoli with Parmesan

level	technique	prep	cook	serves
Basic	Boil pg. 22, Sauté pg. 18	10 min	20 min	4

♦ 3   cups broccoli florets

1¼ teaspoons salt

♦ 1   cup (about 3 ounces) whole wheat penne

2   teaspoons olive oil

4   garlic cloves, chopped

♦ ½   cup Chicken Stock (page 32) or store-bought
reduced-sodium chicken broth

¼   cup grated Parmesan cheese

1 Bring large pot water to boil. Add broccoli and 1 teaspoon of the salt; cook until bright green, about 2 minutes. Transfer with slotted spoon to colander and rinse under cold running water; drain well.

2 Return water to boil. Add penne and cook according to package directions. Drain.

3 Meanwhile, heat oil in a large nonstick skillet over medium-high heat. Add garlic; cook, stirring constantly, just until garlic begins to brown, about 1 minute. Add broth and bring to a boil. Add the broccoli, penne, and remaining ¼ teaspoon salt; cook, stirring frequently, until heated through, about 2 minutes. Transfer to serving plate; sprinkle with Parmesan.

PER SERVING (about ¾ cup): 136 Cal, 4 g Fat, 2 g Sat Fat, 0 g Trans Fat, 5 mg Chol, 403 mg Sod, 17 g Carb, 4 g Fib, 8 g Prot, 87 mg Calc.

CHAPTER 10

Sweets & Treats

With these perfectly light desserts, you can treat yourself and still stay on plan. You'll find cakes worthy of a celebration, pies to die for, a comforting rice pudding, and fresh-from-the-oven cookies for the kid in each of us. Whatever the occasion or the craving (chocolate, anyone?), you'll find a sweet to satisfy every taste.

Banana-Cardamom Cake with Cream Cheese Frosting (5 POINTS VALUE)

level	technique	prep	cook	serves
Intermediate	Bake pg. 27	25 min	30 min	16

CAKE

- 2 cups all-purpose flour
- 3/4 cup granulated sugar
- 1 teaspoon ground cardamom
- 2 teaspoons baking powder
- 1/2 teaspoon baking soda
- 1/2 teaspoon salt
- 3/4 cup low-fat buttermilk
- ♦ 2 ripe medium bananas, mashed (1 cup)
- ♦ 2 large eggs
- ♦ 1 large egg white
- 1/3 cup canola oil
- 1 teaspoon vanilla extract

FROSTING

- 1 (8-ounce) package light cream cheese (Neufchâtel), at room temperature
- 1/2 cup confectioners' sugar
- 3 tablespoons low-fat (1%) milk
- 1 teaspoon vanilla extract

1 Preheat oven to 350°F. Spray 9 x 13-inch baking pan with nonstick spray.

2 To make cake, whisk together flour, granulated sugar, cardamom, baking powder, baking soda, and salt in medium bowl. Whisk together remaining cake ingredients in separate medium bowl. Gradually add buttermilk mixture to flour mixture, stirring just until blended.

3 Pour batter into pan. Bake until toothpick inserted into center comes out clean, 30–35 minutes. Let cool in pan on wire rack 10 minutes. Run thin knife around the edge of cake to loosen it from pan. Remove cake from pan and let cool completely on rack.

4 Meanwhile, to make frosting, with an electric mixer on high speed, beat all frosting ingredients in medium bowl until smooth, about 1 minute. With narrow metal spatula, spread frosting over top of cake.

PER SERVING (1/16 of cake): 216 Cal, 9 g Fat, 3 g Sat Fat, 0 g Trans Fat, 38 mg Chol, 295 mg Sod, 30 g Carb, 1 g Fib, 5 g Prot, 68 mg Calc.

Cranberry-Orange Loaf Cake

5 POINTS VALUE

level	technique	prep	cook	serves
Basic	Bake pg. 27	20 min	1 hr 10 min	12

- 2 cups all-purpose flour
- 1 tablespoon grated orange zest
- 1 teaspoon baking powder
- ½ teaspoon baking soda
- ½ teaspoon salt
- 6 tablespoons unsalted butter, softened
- 1¼ cups sugar
- ♦ ⅔ cup fat-free egg substitute
- 1 teaspoon vanilla extract
- ½ cup reduced-fat sour cream, at room temperature
- ♦ 1 cup fresh or frozen cranberries

1 Preheat oven to 350°F. Spray 4½ x 8½-inch loaf pan with nonstick spray.

2 Whisk together flour, orange zest, baking powder, baking soda, and salt in medium bowl. With an electric mixer on medium speed, beat butter until creamy, about 1 minute. Add sugar and beat until light and fluffy, about 4 minutes. Reduce speed to low. Gradually beat in egg substitute. Beat in vanilla. Alternately add flour mixture and sour cream, beginning and ending with flour mixture and beating just until blended. Gently fold in cranberries.

3 Scrape batter into pan; spread evenly. Bake until toothpick inserted into center comes out clean, about 1 hour 10 minutes. Let cool in pan on wire rack 10 minutes. Remove cake from pan and let cool completely on rack.

PER SERVING (¹⁄₁₂ of cake): 232 Cal, 7 g Fat, 4 g Sat Fat, 0 g Trans Fat, 19 mg Chol, 223 mg Sod, 39 g Carb, 1 g Fib, 4 g Prot, 62 mg Calc.

IN THE KITCHEN

When buying citrus to zest, look for fruit that is unblemished and that shows no signs of shriveling. Most citrus has a coating of wax on the outside. To remove it before zesting, scrub the fruit with a vegetable brush and rinse well.

HOW TO...
Measure Dry Ingredients

To measure flour, confectioners' sugar, granulated sugar, or cocoa, spoon the ingredient into the dry measuring cup until heaping full. Level it off with the straight edge of a knife. Do not pack or shake the cup.

To measure brown sugar, firmly pack the sugar into a dry measuring cup, then level it off with your fingertips or the straight edge of a knife.

Apple Butter Fruit Cake with Walnut Streusel Topping (5 POINTS VALUE)

level	technique	prep	cook	serves
Basic	Bake pg. 27	20 min	35 min	20

TOPPING

- ¼ cup chopped walnuts
- 3 tablespoons all-purpose flour
- 3 tablespoons packed light brown sugar
- 2 tablespoons canola oil
- ½ teaspoon cinnamon

CAKE

- 2 cups all-purpose flour
- 2 teaspoons baking powder
- 1 teaspoon cinnamon
- ½ teaspoon baking soda
- ¼ teaspoon ground cloves
- ♦ 3 large eggs
- 1 cup packed light brown sugar
- 1 cup apple butter
- ⅓ cup canola oil
- 1 teaspoon vanilla extract
- ½ cup dried apricots, finely chopped
- ½ cup golden raisins

1 Preheat oven to 350°F. Line an 8-inch square baking pan with foil, allowing foil to extend over rim of pan by 2 inches. Spray with nonstick spray.

2 To make topping, stir together topping ingredients in small bowl until moistened.

3 To make cake, whisk together flour, baking powder, cinnamon, baking soda, and cloves in medium bowl. With an electric mixer on high speed, beat eggs in large bowl until thickened, about 2 minutes. Gradually add brown sugar, beating until light and fluffy, about 3 minutes. Reduce speed to low. Beat in apple butter, oil, and vanilla until combined. Add flour mixture and beat just until blended. Stir in apricots and raisins.

4 Pour batter into pan; sprinkle evenly with topping. Bake until toothpick inserted into center comes out clean, 35–40 minutes. Let cool completely in pan on wire rack. Lift out using foil as handles.

PER SERVING (1/20 of cake): 213 Cal, 7 g Fat, 1 g Sat Fat, 0 g Trans Fat, 32 mg Chol, 95 mg Sod, 36 g Carb, 1 g Fib, 3 g Prot, 53 mg Calc.

APPLE BUTTER FRUIT CAKE WITH WALNUT STREUSEL TOPPING

Sour Cream–Pecan Bundt Cake

5 POINTS VALUE

level	technique	prep	cook	serves
Intermediate	Bake pg. 27	25 min	40 min	16

½ cup pecans, chopped
½ cup packed light brown sugar
1½ teaspoons cinnamon
½ teaspoon ground cloves
¼ teaspoon nutmeg
1½ cups whole wheat pastry flour
1 cup all-purpose flour
2 teaspoons baking powder
½ teaspoon baking soda
½ teaspoon salt
4 tablespoons unsalted butter, softened
1⅓ cups granulated sugar
♦ 2 large eggs
♦ 2 large egg whites
♦ 1¼ cups fat-free sour cream
2 teaspoons vanilla extract
1 teaspoon confectioners' sugar

1 Preheat oven to 350°F. Spray 10-inch Bundt pan with nonstick spray.

2 Evenly sprinkle 2 tablespoons pecans in bottom of pan. Combine remaining pecans, brown sugar, cinnamon, cloves, and nutmeg in small bowl. Whisk together pastry flour, all-purpose flour, baking powder, baking soda, and salt in medium bowl.

3 With an electric mixer on medium speed, beat butter and ⅓ cup granulated sugar in large bowl until light and fluffy, about 2 minutes. Gradually beat in remaining 1 cup granulated sugar, then beat 1 minute longer. Beat in eggs and egg whites, one at a time, beating well after each addition. Beat in sour cream and vanilla. Reduce mixer speed to low. Gradually add flour mixture, beating just until blended.

4 Spoon one third of batter into pan; spread evenly. Sprinkle evenly with half of pecan mixture. Spoon half of remaining batter on top; spread evenly. Sprinkle with remaining brown sugar mixture. Spoon remaining batter on top; spread evenly. Bake until toothpick inserted into center comes out clean, 40–45 minutes. Let cool in pan on wire rack 10 minutes. Remove cake from pan and let cool completely on rack. Dust with confectioners' sugar.

PER SERVING (1/16 of cake): 233 Cal, 6 g Fat, 2 g Sat Fat, 0 g Trans Fat, 36 mg Chol, 219 mg Sod, 42 g Carb, 2 g Fib, 5 g Prot, 78 mg Calc.

HOW TO...
Separate an Egg

1

Sharply tap an egg along its middle with a dinner knife to make a crosswise crack.

2

Separate the shell halves with your thumbs and allow the whites to run into a bowl, passing the yolk back and forth from one shell-half to the other. Drop the yolk into another bowl.

Toasted Coconut Cream Pie

level	technique	prep	cook	serves
Intermediate	Bake pg. 27	20 min	15 min	8

CRUST

15 reduced-fat gingersnap cookies

1 tablespoon + 2 teaspoons canola oil

1 tablespoon chopped almonds

FILLING

1 envelope unflavored gelatin

¼ cup cold water

¼ cup sugar

3 tablespoons all-purpose flour

1 cup low-fat (1%) milk

½ cup light coconut milk

♦ 1 large egg

Pinch salt

1 teaspoon coconut extract

½ cup thawed frozen light whipped topping

2 tablespoons flaked sweetened coconut, toasted

1 Preheat oven to 375°F. Spray 9-inch pie plate with nonstick spray.

2 To make crust, put gingersnaps in food processor and pulse until finely ground. Add oil and almonds; process until crumbly. Press crumb mixture evenly onto bottom and up side of pie plate. Bake until set, 8–10 minutes. Let cool completely on wire rack.

3 To make filling, sprinkle gelatin over water in microwavable cup. Let stand until softened, about 5 minutes. Microwave on High until gelatin is completely dissolved, about 15 seconds.

4 Whisk together sugar and flour in medium saucepan. Whisk in milk, coconut milk, egg, and salt and set over medium-high heat. Cook, stirring constantly, until mixture thickens, about 4 minutes (do not let boil). Remove saucepan from heat. Stir in gelatin mixture and coconut extract. Pour into medium bowl; refrigerate until filling begins to set, about 30 minutes. Whisk until smooth and creamy. With rubber spatula, gently fold in whipped topping. Pour into crust and sprinkle with toasted coconut. Refrigerate until firm, at least 2 hours or up to 6 hours.

PER SERVING (⅛ of pie): 168 Cal, 7 g Fat, 2 g Sat Fat, 0 g Trans Fat, 28 mg Chol, 150 mg Sod, 23 g Carb, 1 g Fib, 4 g Prot, 58 mg Calc.

PEANUT BUTTER AND
CHOCOLATE CUPCAKES

Peanut Butter and Chocolate Cupcakes ③ POINTS VALUE

level	technique	prep	cook	serves
Basic	Bake pg. 27	20 min	25 min	24

FROSTING

- ½ cup light cream cheese (Neufchâtel), softened
- ¼ cup reduced-fat creamy peanut butter
- ¼ cup confectioners' sugar

CUPCAKES

- 1 cup cake flour
- 1 cup granulated sugar
- ½ cup unsweetened cocoa powder
- 1 teaspoon baking powder
- ¼ teaspoon baking soda
- ¼ teaspoon salt
- ½ cup low-fat buttermilk
- ⅓ cup canola oil
- ♦ 1 large egg
- ♦ 1 large egg white
- 1 teaspoon vanilla extract
- 1 ounce semisweet chocolate, melted and cooled
- ¼ cup unsalted roasted peanuts, chopped

1 Preheat oven to 350°F. Spray 24-cup mini-muffin pan with nonstick spray.

2 To make frosting, with an electric mixer on low speed, beat frosting ingredients in small bowl until smooth, about 2 minutes. Cover with plastic wrap.

3 To make cupcakes, whisk together cake flour, granulated sugar, cocoa, baking powder, baking soda, and salt in medium bowl. Whisk together buttermilk, oil, egg, egg white, and vanilla in large bowl. Whisk in melted chocolate. Add flour mixture, stirring just until blended.

4 Fill each muffin cup two thirds full with batter. Bake until toothpick inserted into center comes out clean, about 25 minutes. Let cool in pan on wire rack 10 minutes. Remove cupcakes from pan and let cool completely on rack.

5 With small metal spatula, spread frosting over tops of cupcakes; sprinkle with peanuts.

PER SERVING (1 cupcake): 138 Cal, 7 g Fat, 2 g Sat Fat, 0 g Trans Fat, 13 mg Chol, 105 mg Sod, 18 g Carb, 1 g Fib, 4 g Prot, 28 mg Calc.

Double Chocolate Almond Pie

level	technique	prep	cook	serves
Intermediate	Simmer pg. 22, Bake pg. 27	30 min	20 min	12

FILLING

- 1½ cups low-fat (1%) milk
- ♦ 1 large egg
- ½ cup sugar
- ¼ cup all-purpose flour
- ¼ teaspoon salt
- ¼ cup semisweet chocolate chips
- ½ teaspoon almond extract
- 1 (6-ounce) prepared chocolate cookie crust

MERINGUE TOPPING

- ♦ 4 large egg whites
- ½ teaspoon cream of tartar
- ½ cup sugar
- ¼ teaspoon almond extract
- 1 tablespoon chopped almonds, toasted

1 Preheat oven to 375°F.

2 To make filling, whisk together milk, egg, sugar, flour, and salt in medium saucepan, then set over medium-high heat. Cook, stirring constantly, until mixture thickens and coats back of spoon, about 4 minutes (do not let boil or mixture may curdle). Remove saucepan from heat; stir in chocolate chips and almond extract until chocolate is melted and mixture is smooth. Pour into crust.

3 To make meringue, with an electric mixer on medium speed, beat egg whites and cream of tartar in large bowl until soft peaks form. Increase speed to medium-high. Sprinkle in sugar, 1 tablespoon at a time, beating until stiff, glossy peaks form. Beat in almond extract.

4 Spoon meringue over filling, spreading it to edge of crust to completely enclose filling; sprinkle with almonds. Bake until meringue is golden brown, about 15 minutes. Let cool on wire rack about 1 hour. Refrigerate at least 3 hours or up to 6 hours. This pie is best eaten the day it is prepared.

PER SERVING (¹⁄₁₂ of pie): 195 Cal, 7 g Fat, 2 g Sat Fat, 0 g Trans Fat, 21 mg Chol, 163 mg Sod, 31 g Carb, 1 g Fib, 4 g Prot, 46 mg Calc.

Pear and Cranberry Crisp (4 POINTS VALUE)

level	technique	prep	cook	serves
Basic	Bake pg. 27	20 min	55 min	8

½ cup + 2 tablespoons all-purpose flour

♦ ½ cup quick-cooking (not instant) or old-fashioned oats

½ cup sugar

¼ teaspoon cinnamon

⅛ teaspoon salt

3 tablespoons cold unsalted butter, diced

1 teaspoon water

♦ 3 pounds pears, peeled and thinly sliced

♦ ¾ cup fresh or frozen cranberries

1 teaspoon grated peeled fresh ginger

1 teaspoon vanilla extract

1 Preheat oven to 375°F. Spray 7 x 11-inch baking dish with nonstick spray.

2 To make topping, combine ½ cup flour, oats, ¼ cup sugar, cinnamon, and salt in medium bowl. Add butter and pinch with your fingers to form coarse crumbs. Add water and firmly press mixture to form clumps.

3 Combine pears, cranberries, remaining ¼ cup sugar and 2 tablespoons flour, ginger, and vanilla in large bowl; mix well. Transfer to baking dish. Sprinkle topping over fruit. Bake until filling is bubbly and topping is golden, 55 minutes–1 hour. Serve warm or at room temperature.

PER SERVING (about ¾ cup): 239 Cal, 5 g Fat, 3 g Sat Fat, 0 g Trans Fat, 11 mg Chol, 38 mg Sod, 49 g Carb, 6 g Fib, 2 g Prot, 21 mg Calc.

IN THE KITCHEN

Bartlett pears are the most commonly available and usually the most economical, although any type of pear will work in this recipe. For cooking, choose pears that are firm and just slightly underripe.

Blueberry-Nectarine Tart with Phyllo Crust (2 POINTS VALUE)

level	technique	prep	cook	serves
Intermediate	Bake pg. 27	30 min	45 min	10

¼ cup packed light brown sugar

1 tablespoon all-purpose flour

¼ teaspoon nutmeg

Pinch salt

♦ 4 ripe medium nectarines, halved, pitted, and sliced

♦ 1 cup blueberries

1 tablespoon grated lemon zest (about 2 lemons)

6 (12 x 17-inch) sheets frozen phyllo dough, thawed

1 tablespoon unsalted butter, melted

1 Preheat oven to 375°F. Spray 10-inch pizza pan or large baking sheet with nonstick spray.

2 Combine brown sugar, flour, nutmeg, and salt in large bowl. Add nectarines, blueberries, and lemon zest; toss to mix well.

3 Lay 1 phyllo sheet in pan; lightly spray with nonstick spray. Keep remaining phyllo covered with damp paper towel and plastic wrap to keep it from drying out. Working quickly, repeat with remaining 5 phyllo sheets, placing corners at different angles and lightly spraying each sheet with nonstick spray. Roll up edges of phyllo to form 1½-inch-wide rim.

4 Spoon nectarine mixture evenly on top of phyllo and drizzle with melted butter. Bake until edges of phyllo are golden brown and nectarines are tender, about 45 minutes. Let cool on wire rack about 1 hour before serving.

PER SERVING (¹⁄₁₀ of tart): 102 Cal, 1 g Fat, 1 g Sat Fat, 0 g Trans Fat, 3 mg Chol, 81 mg Sod, 21 g Carb, 1 g Fib, 2 g Prot, 13 mg Calc.

IN THE KITCHEN

Ripe fruit will give the best flavor when making this tart. To choose the most flavorful nectarines, select those that are yellow with a blush of pink and that give slightly to palm pressure.

**BLUEBERRY-NECTARINE
TART WITH PHYLLO CRUST**

Roasted Pineapple with Mint and Lime (1) POINTS VALUE

level	technique	prep	cook	serves
Basic	Roast pg. 24	5 min	15 min	4

- ◆ 1 peeled and cored pineapple
- 1½ teaspoons canola oil
- ½ teaspoon cinnamon
- ⅛ teaspoon ground cloves
- 1 tablespoon fresh lime juice
- 1 tablespoon chopped fresh mint

1 Preheat oven to 500°F. Spray large baking sheet with nonstick spray.

2 Cut pineapple into 16 slices. Lightly brush both sides of each slice with oil; sprinkle with cinnamon and cloves.

3 Place pineapple on baking sheet. Roast until tender, about 12 minutes. Remove pineapple from oven; increase oven temperature to broil. Brush pineapple with lime juice and broil 5 inches from heat until lightly browned on edges, 1–2 minutes. Serve warm or at room temperature. Sprinkle with mint just before serving.

PER SERVING (4 slices): 75 Cal, 2 g Fat, 0 g Sat Fat, 0 g Trans Fat, 0 mg Chol, 1 mg Sod, 15 g Carb, 2 g Fib, 1 g Prot, 10 mg Calc.

IN THE KITCHEN

If you don't have fresh mint, this healthful dessert is just as good without it. This recipe works with the Simply Filling technique.

Fruit Salad with Citrus-Basil Syrup

2 POINTS VALUE

level	technique	prep	cook	serves
Basic	Simmer pg. 22	20 min	5 min	8

¼ cup fresh orange juice

¼ cup fresh lime juice

1 tablespoon sugar

½ cup thinly sliced fresh basil

♦ 3 cups peeled and cubed fresh pineapple

♦ 2 bananas, cut into 1-inch pieces

♦ 2 kiwifruit, peeled and cut into ¼-inch slices

♦ 2 oranges, peeled, halved, and cut into ¼-inch slices

♦ 1 small papaya, peeled, pitted, and cut into ³/₄-inch cubes

♦ 1 cup fresh blueberries

1 Combine orange juice, lime juice, and sugar in small saucepan; bring just to simmer over medium heat. Remove from heat and stir in ¼ cup basil. Let cool. Strain through fine-mesh sieve into large bowl; discard basil.

2 Add pineapple, bananas, kiwi, oranges, papaya, and blueberries to juice mixture; toss to coat. Refrigerate until chilled and flavors are blended, about 30 minutes. Stir in remaining ¼ cup basil just before serving.

PER SERVING (about 1½ cups): 151 Cal, 1 g Fat, 0 g Sat Fat, 0 g Trans Fat, 0 mg Chol, 5 mg Sod, 39 g Carb, 5 g Fib, 2 g Prot, 52 mg Calc.

IN THE KITCHEN

The flavorful citrus and basil syrup is delicious on any kind of fruit. Modify the mixture of fruits in this recipe based on what's in season and what you like best.

Tips for Measuring Ingredients

If you measure carefully and correctly, you will get consistent results each time you cook.

Brown Sugar Firmly pack the sugar into a dry measuring cup, then level it off with the straight edge of a knife.

Butter The wrapper that butter comes in is premarked for tablespoons, ¼ cup, ⅓ cup, and ½ cup, so there is no need to measure it.

Dry Ingredients Use standard dry measuring cups that come in nesting sets of ¼, ⅓, ½, and 1 cup. To measure flour, first stir it to aerate, then lightly spoon into the desired size cup to overflowing. Level it off with the straight edge of a knife.

Liquids Place a glass measuring cup with a spout on the counter and add the desired amount of liquid. Bend down to check the amount at eye level.

Sour Cream and Yogurt Use standard dry measuring cups. Spoon the ingredient into a cup, and level it off with a rubber spatula.

Spices, Herbs, Citrus Zest, and Extract Use standard measuring spoons that come in nesting sets of ¼, ½, and 1 teaspoon and 1 tablespoon. Fill the desired spoon with the ingredient, then level it off with the straight edge of a knife.

Coconut-Ginger Rice Pudding

level	technique	prep	cook	serves
Basic	Simmer pg. 22	20 min	1 hr	8

2½ cups water

Pinch salt

1 cup long-grain white rice, preferably jasmine or basmati

2 cups low-fat (1%) milk

1 (14-ounce) can light coconut milk

¼ cup packed light brown sugar

¼ cup granulated sugar

2 teaspoons grated peeled fresh ginger

¼ cup shredded sweetened coconut, toasted

1 Bring water and salt to boil in heavy medium saucepan over high heat. Add rice and reduce heat to low. Cook, covered, 20 minutes. Remove saucepan from heat and let stand, covered, about 10 minutes.

2 Stir milk, coconut milk, brown sugar, granulated sugar, and ginger into rice and set over medium heat; bring just to boil. Reduce heat to low and simmer, stirring frequently, until mixture is thick and creamy and rice is very soft, about 30 minutes, stirring constantly during last 5 minutes of cooking.

3 Spoon rice pudding into medium bowl and let cool to room temperature, stirring occasionally. Refrigerate, covered, until chilled, at least 4 hours or up to overnight.

4 Spoon pudding evenly into 8 dessert dishes. Top evenly with coconut.

PER SERVING (½ cup pudding with ½ tablespoon coconut): 202 Cal, 4 g Fat, 3 g Sat Fat, 0 g Trans Fat, 3 mg Chol, 88 mg Sod, 38 g Carb, 1 g Fib, 4 g Prot, 86 mg Calc.

◆ FILLING EXTRA

Top each serving of the pudding with ½ cup sliced mango. The per-serving **POINTS** value will increase by **1**.

White Chocolate Chunk Oatmeal Cookies ②
POINTS VALUE

level	technique	prep	cook	serves
Basic	Bake pg. 27	15 min	10 min	24

- ♦ ½ cup quick-cooking (not instant) oats
- 1 cup all-purpose flour
- ½ teaspoon baking soda
- ¼ teaspoon salt
- 4 tablespoons unsalted butter, melted and cooled
- ¾ cup packed light brown sugar
- ♦ 1 large egg
- 1 teaspoon vanilla extract
- 4 ounces white chocolate, cut into ¼-inch pieces

1 Place oven racks in upper and lower thirds of oven and preheat oven to 350°F. Spray 2 large baking sheets with nonstick spray.

2 Put oats in blender and process until finely ground. Combine oats, flour, baking soda, and salt in small bowl. With an electric mixer on low speed, beat butter, brown sugar, egg, and vanilla in large bowl until well blended. Add flour mixture and beat until blended. Stir chocolate into dough.

3 Drop dough by level tablespoonfuls onto baking sheets 2 inches apart. With glass dipped in flour or with your fingers, press each mound to make 2-inch rounds. Bake until lightly browned along edges, 9–11 minutes, rotating baking sheets halfway through baking. Let cool on baking sheets on wire racks about 1 minute. With spatula, transfer cookies to racks and let cool completely.

PER SERVING (1 cookie): 98 Cal, 4 g Fat, 2 g Sat Fat, 0 g Trans Fat, 15 mg Chol, 60 mg Sod, 15 g Carb, 0 g Fib, 1 g Prot, 18 mg Calc.

FROM TOP, CLOCKWISE: BROWN
BUTTER–SPICE COOKIES, PAGE 240,
CHOCOLATE-CHERRY BISCOTTI WITH
CHOCOLATE DRIZZLE, PAGE 241,
AND APRICOT-ALMOND SQUARES

Apricot-Almond Squares (3 POINTS VALUE)

level	technique	prep	cook	serves
Basic	Bake pg. 27	20 min	25 min	16

- 1 cup whole wheat pastry flour
- ◆ ¾ cup quick-cooking (not instant) oats
- ½ cup packed light brown sugar
- ¼ cup slivered almonds, finely chopped
- ½ teaspoon cinnamon
- ½ teaspoon baking soda
- ¼ teaspoon salt
- ◆ 1 large egg white
- 2 tablespoons canola oil
- ◆ 1 tablespoon fat-free milk
- 1 (10-ounce) jar apricot fruit spread
- ½ cup chopped dried apricots

1 Preheat oven to 350°F. Line 9-inch square baking pan with foil, allowing foil to extend over rim of pan by 2 inches. Spray foil with nonstick spray.

2 Combine pastry flour, oats, brown sugar, almonds, cinnamon, baking soda, and salt in large bowl. With fork, beat together egg white, oil, and milk in small bowl. Add egg mixture to flour mixture, stirring until well blended. With your fingers, blend mixture until moist crumbs form. Reserve ⅔ cup. Transfer remaining oat mixture to pan, pressing firmly to form an even layer. Bake until set and lightly browned along edges, about 10 minutes.

3 Stir together fruit spread and apricots in small bowl; spread evenly over hot crust. Crumble reserved oat mixture on top. Bake until fruit spread is bubbly at edges and top is browned, 15–20 minutes. Let cool completely in pan on wire rack. Lift out using foil as handles; cut into 16 squares.

PER SERVING (1 square): 146 Cal, 3 g Fat, 0 g Sat Fat, 0 g Trans Fat, 0 mg Chol, 85 mg Sod, 29 g Carb, 3 g Fib, 3 g Prot, 25 mg Calc.

IN THE KITCHEN

Whole wheat pastry flour is made from very finely ground soft white wheat. It gives a lighter texture and a more tender crumb in baked goods than regular whole wheat flour, even though it contains almost the same amount of fiber and other nutrients. Look for it in a natural foods store or a well-stocked supermarket.

Brown Butter–Spice Cookies

level	technique	prep	cook	makes
Basic	Bake pg. 27	20 min	10 min	36

4 tablespoons unsalted butter

1½ cups all-purpose flour

½ teaspoon cinnamon

¼ teaspoon ground cloves

¼ teaspoon ground allspice

½ teaspoon baking soda

½ teaspoon salt

¾ cup packed dark brown sugar

¼ cup honey

♦ 1 large egg white

2 teaspoons vanilla extract

♦ ⅓ cup fat-free sour cream

1 Place oven racks in upper and lower thirds of oven and preheat oven to 350°F. Spray 2 large baking sheets with nonstick spray.

2 Melt butter in small saucepan over low heat. Continue to cook, swirling pan occasionally, until butter turns nut brown, about 2 minutes. Pour butter into small bowl and let cool to room temperature.

3 Whisk together flour, cinnamon, cloves, allspice, baking soda, and salt in small bowl. Stir together brown sugar, honey, egg white, and vanilla in large bowl until blended. Stir in browned butter, then sour cream. Add flour mixture and stir until blended. Drop dough by teaspoonfuls onto baking sheets about 2 inches apart. Bake until cookies spring back when lightly pressed, 8–10 minutes, rotating baking sheets halfway through baking. Let cool on baking sheets on wire racks about 2 minutes. With spatula, transfer cookies to racks and let cool completely.

PER SERVING (1 cookie): 58 Cal, 1 g Fat, 1 g Sat Fat, 0 g Trans Fat, 4 mg Chol, 57 mg Sod, 10 g Carb, 0 g Fib, 1 g Prot, 9 mg Calc.

Chocolate-Cherry Biscotti with Chocolate Drizzle

1 POINTS VALUE

level	technique	prep	cook	makes
Intermediate	Bake, pg. 27	15 min	35 min	60

1½ cups all-purpose flour
½ cup unsweetened cocoa powder
2 teaspoons baking powder
½ teaspoon baking soda
¼ teaspoon salt
¾ cup sugar
♦ 2 large eggs
2 tablespoons unsalted butter, melted
1 teaspoon vanilla extract
¾ cup dried cherries
1 ounce semisweet chocolate

1 Preheat oven to 350°F. Spray large baking sheet with nonstick spray.

2 Combine flour, cocoa, baking powder, baking soda, and salt in large bowl. With an electric mixer on medium speed, beat sugar, eggs, butter, and vanilla in medium bowl. Reduce speed to low. Add flour mixture to egg mixture until well combined (the dough will be fairly dry). Add cherries, kneading dough a few times in bowl if necessary.

3 Sprinkle work surface lightly with flour. Turn dough onto surface and divide in half. With floured hands, working 1 piece at a time, roll dough with palms of your hands into 15 x 1½-inch log. Place log on baking sheet. Repeat with remaining dough, placing logs 2 inches apart. Bake until firm and toothpick inserted into center of each log comes out clean, about 15 minutes. With wide spatula, carefully transfer logs to cutting board; let cool 10 minutes.

4 Meanwhile, reduce oven temperature to 300°F. With serrated knife, slice each log crosswise into 30 (½-inch-thick) slices. Place slices 1 inch apart on baking sheet. Bake until fairly dry, about 10 minutes on each side. Cool completely on wire rack.

5 Place chocolate in small microwavable bowl and microwave on High, stirring every 15 seconds, until melted and smooth, 45 seconds–1 minute. Transfer chocolate to small zip-close plastic bag. Cut off tiny corner of bag and decoratively drizzle chocolate over cookies. Refrigerate or let stand in cool place until chocolate is firm.

PER SERVING (3 cookies): 38 Cal, 1 g Fat, 0 g Sat Fat, 0 g Trans Fat, 8 mg Chol, 39 mg Sod, 7 g Carb, 0 g Fib, 1 g Prot, 13 mg Calc.

What it Means

Understand the basic baking terms used in recipes and you'll soon be baking like a pro.

Beat To combine ingredients while incorporating air using a wooden spoon, fork, handheld mixer, or stand mixer.

Blend To combine two or more ingredients.

Caramelize To heat sugar until it is melted and browned.

Combine To stir two or more ingredients together until mixed.

Cream To beat butter or cream cheese until creamy or butter and sugar until light and fluffy.

Cut In When making pastry dough, to cut fat into the flour mixture until pea-sized using a pastry blender or two knives used scissor-fashion.

Drizzle To drip a glaze or icing over a cake or other baked good.

Fold In To gently combine a light mixture with a heavier one without losing volume.

Mix To combine two or more ingredients.

Mix Until Moistened To combine a liquid with dry ingredients just until the dry ingredients are evenly and thoroughly moistened. The mixture is often lumpy.

Soften Recipes often call for softened butter for easy blending or beating. Leave the butter out at room temperature for about 30 minutes until pliable—not greasy or melting.

Soft Peaks To beat egg whites until rounded peaks form when the beaters are lifted.

Stiff Peaks To beat egg whites until pointed peaks form when the beaters are lifted.

Zest The flavorful, colorful outer peel of citrus fruit.

Frozen Mocha Pie ④

level	technique	prep	cook	serves
Intermediate	Bake pg. 27	30 min	10 min	12

CRUST

- 9 whole (2½ x 5-inch) chocolate graham crackers
- 2 tablespoons honey
- 1 tablespoon canola oil
- 1 tablespoon low-fat (1%) milk

FILLING

- 2 pints fat-free chocolate ice cream, slightly softened
- 1 pint fat-free coffee ice cream, slightly softened
- ¾ cup Rich Chocolate Sauce (page 44) or store-bought light chocolate syrup
- 2 ounces semisweet chocolate, chopped

1 Preheat oven to 375°F. Spray 9-inch pie plate with nonstick spray.

2 To make crust, put graham crackers in food processor and pulse until finely ground. Add honey, oil, and milk; process until moist and crumbly. Press crumb mixture evenly onto bottom and up side of pie plate. Bake until firm, 8–10 minutes. Let cool completely on wire rack, then freeze until firm, about 30 minutes.

3 To make filling, with narrow metal spatula, spread 2 cups chocolate ice cream in crust in an even layer; freeze until firm, about 30 minutes. Spread coffee ice cream on top of chocolate ice cream; freeze until firm, about 30 minutes. Spread remaining chocolate ice cream on top of coffee ice cream. Loosely wrap pie in wax paper and then in heavy-duty foil. Freeze until completely frozen, at least 4 hours or up to 1 week.

4 Let pie soften slightly in refrigerator about 15 minutes. Cut pie into 12 wedges and place on plates. Drizzle each serving with 1 tablespoon sauce and sprinkle evenly with chocolate. Serve at once.

PER SERVING (1/12 of pie): 215 Cal, 5 g Fat, 2 g Sat Fat, 0 g Trans Fat, 2 mg Chol, 157 mg Sod, 41 g Carb, 2 g Fib, 5 g Prot, 125 mg Calc.

◆ FILLING EXTRA

For a presentation that's pretty and healthful, serve each wedge of the pie with a handful of raspberries.

FROZEN MOCHA PIE

Index

C

Recipes by *POINTS* value

0 POINTS value

Go-with-Everything Pico de Gallo, 40

Pineapple-Poblano Salsa, 55

Steamed Asparagus with Tarragon Gremolata, 202

Vegetable Stock, 30

1 POINTS value

Asian Lime Vinaigrette, 35

Beef Stock, 31

Brown Butter–Spice Cookies, 240

Buttermilk–Herb Dressing, 38

Chicken Stock, 32

Chocolate-Cherry Biscotti with Chocolate Drizzle, 241

Creamy Balsamic Dressing, 39

Creamy Custard Sauce, 45

Homemade Marinara Sauce, 34

No-Cook Raspberry Sauce, 43

Red Wine–Shallot Vinaigrette, 37

Roasted Pineapple with Mint and Lime, 234

Roasted Tomatoes with Rosemary and Balsamic Vinegar, 203

Salad-Stuffed Mushrooms, 211

Smoky Red Peppers with Capers, 204

Spinach-Basil Pesto Sauce, 42

Spinach with Grapes and Pine Nuts, 207

Swiss Chard with Caramelized Garlic and Grape Tomatoes, 206

2 POINTS value

Basmati Rice with Green Beans and Shallots, 218

Blueberry-Nectarine Tart with Phyllo Crust, 232

Broccoli and Red Apple Salad, 58

Butternut Squash Soup with Pear and Cheese Toasts, 61

Caribbean Shrimp Salad, 170

Creamy Broccoli-Lemon Soup, 59

Fruit Salad with Citrus-Basil Syrup, 235

Mixed Green Salad with Avocado and Roasted Corn, 57

Moroccan Carrot Dip with Toasted Pita Triangles, 54

Orange-Glazed Cranberry Scones, 79

Penne and Broccoli with Parmesan, 219

Rich Chocolate Sauce, 44

Shrimp Cocktail with Smoky Tomato Salsa, 53

Tex-Mex–Style Black Bean Burgers, 182

White Chocolate Chunk Oatmeal Cookies, 237

3 POINTS value

Apricot-Almond Squares, 239

Bombay Shrimp Salad, 170

Chicken and Goat Cheese Quesadillas, 51

Ginger-Soy Glazed Chicken Skewers, 50

Grilled Beef, Spinach, and Feta Bruschetta, 48

Grilled Pork with Tamarind Sauce, 122

Lamb Chops with Artichokes, Garlic, and Mint, 129

Lemon Corn Muffins with Raspberries, 78

Lemon-Pepper Shrimp, 170

Peanut Butter and Chocolate Cupcakes, 229

Potato-Leek Mash, 209

Quinoa with Squash and Cranberries, 217

Roasted Eggplant–Tomato Stacks, 212

Shrimp and Spinach Salad with Lemon Dressing, 172

Spiced Fruit Compote, 74

Spicy Soy-Glazed Sweet Potatoes, 210

Sweet Potato and Ham Hash, 67

Tuna and White Bean Crostini, 52

Turkey Cutlets with Lemon, 151

White Bean Stew with Crisp Pancetta and Rosemary, 183

White Beans and Greens, 214

4 POINTS value

Asian Beef and Bok Choy Salad, 111

Baked Egg Cups with Roasted Vegetables, 68

Broiled Flank Steak with Fennel-Coriander Rub, 84

Bulgur Pilaf with Dates and Apricots, 216

Buttermilk-Maple Bran Muffins, 76

Chicken and Black Bean Chili, 144

Chickpea, Spinach, and Nectarine Salad, 182

Coconut-Ginger Rice Pudding, 236

Coffee-Braised Chicken Thighs, 146

Cuban-Style Sloppy Joes, 154

Cucumber-Yogurt Chicken, 137

Double Chocolate Almond Pie, 230

Easy Moo Shu Pork, 87

Fresh Apple Coffeecake with Pecan Streusel, 75

Frozen Mocha Pie, 242

Ginger Beef In Lettuce Cups, 116

Honey-Herb Roast Turkey Breast with Pan Gravy, 150

Indian Lentil and Rice Pilaf, 215

Italian Salmon and Bean Salad, 182

Jalapeño Burgers, 116

Lemon-Basil Clam Chowder, 175

Lentils and Rice with Caramelized Onions, 100

Mediterranean Wheat Berry and Tuna Salad, 164

Miso-Crusted Cod, 99

Oven Braised Chicken and Cremini Mushrooms, 135

Pear and Cranberry Crisp, 231

Ricotta Gnocchi with Sage Beurre Blanc, 197

Scallop and Asparagus Stir-Fry, 173

Shrimp-Miso Soup, 170

Spanish Shrimp and Rice Stew, 169

Spiced Mint Chicken, 137

Spinach and Mushroom Frittata with Goat Cheese, 64

Titles in green type represent recipes that work with the Simply Filling technique.

Dry and Liquid Measurement Equivalents

If you are converting the recipes in this book to metric measurements, use the following chart as a guide.

Teaspoons	Tablespoons	Cups	Fluid Ounces
3 teaspoons	1 tablespoon		½ fluid ounce
6 teaspoons	2 tablespoons	⅛ cup	1 fluid ounce
8 teaspoons	2 tablespoons plus 2 teaspoons	⅙ cup	
12 teaspoons	4 tablespoons	¼ cup	2 fluid ounces
15 teaspoons	5 tablespoons	⅓ cup minus 1 teaspoon	
16 teaspoons	5 tablespoons plus 1 teaspoon	⅓ cup	
18 teaspoons	6 tablespoons	¼ cup plus 2 tablespoons	3 fluid ounces
24 teaspoons	8 tablespoons	½ cup	4 fluid ounces
30 teaspoons	10 tablespoons	½ cup plus 2 tablespoons	5 fluid ounces
32 teaspoons	10 tablespoons plus 2 teaspoons	⅔ cup	
36 teaspoons	12 tablespoons	¾ cup	6 fluid ounces
42 teaspoons	14 tablespoons	1 cup minus 2 tablespoons	7 fluid ounces
45 teaspoons	15 tablespoons	1 cup minus 1 tablespoon	
48 teaspoons	16 tablespoons	1 cup	8 fluid ounces

Teaspoons	
¼ teaspoon	1 milliliter
½ teaspoon	2 milliliters
1 teaspoon	5 milliliters
1 tablespoon	15 milliliters
2 tablespoons	30 milliliters
3 tablespoons	45 milliliters
¼ cup	60 milliliters
⅓ cup	80 milliliters
½ cup	120 milliliters
⅔ cup	160 milliliters
¾ cup	175 milliliters
1 cup	240 milliliters
1 quart	950 milliliters

Length

1 inch	25 millimeters
1 inch	2.5 centimeters

Weight

1 ounce	30 grams
¼ pound	120 grams
½ pound	240 grams
1 pound	480 grams

Oven Temperature

250°F	120°C	400°F	200°C
275°F	140°C	425°F	220°C
300°F	150°C	450°F	230°C
325°F	160°C	475°F	250°C
350°F	180°C	500°F	260°C
375°F	190°C	525°F	270°C

Note: Measurement of less than ⅛ teaspoon is considered a dash or a pinch. Metric volume measurements are approximate.